BEING LOVING
is
BEING HEALTHY

BEING LOVING
is
BEING HEALTHY

A Guide to self healing and personal renewal
through the power of Love

by
Paul Lambillion

L. N. Fowler & Co. Ltd.
1201 High Road
Chadwell Health
ROMFORD
Essex RM6 4DH.

First published in 1987 by
L. N. Fowler & Company Ltd.
1201 High Road, Chadwell Health, Romford, Essex, England.

© Paul Lambillion 1987 All rights reserved.

ISBN 085234 378 6

Cover design by Mark Viney : Harrogate

Typeset in Bembo 11/12 point
Printed and bound in the United Kingdom by
Oxford University Printing House.

DEDICATION

To Cyril and Judy for their loving guidance,
To Susan, family and friends for their loving encouragement,
To Renate for her faithful patience,
To lovers of life everywhere . . .
        Thank you.

"I give you a new commandment:
love one another;
just as I have loved you,
you also must love one another."
St. John 13:34.

CONTENTS

INTRODUCTION
BEING LOVING IS BEING HEALTHY
FIRST THOUGHTS

Whilst preparing this book, I called into my local newsagent's shop to have a small piece of writing photocopied. One of the attractive young lady assistants came over to help me, and noticed the content of the paper I handed her — it was "Constructive Living — Your SELF-Healing Programme," copies of which I give to my patients. She casually enquired if I had written or recorded anything for the improvement of confidence and self-esteem, so I mentioned one of my cassette tapes to her. She hesitated for a moment, then turned to me and said, "I am really looking for something that will help me to love myself more."

I was a little surprised by the rather unexpected and direct nature of what she had said. After all, what could an attractive, young, apparently healthy lady, need to be told about loving herself? But within a few moments I realised that everything I seek to do, and indeed most of the things I say and teach, are directed at just that. Whatever the condition, however disease is manifest in a body, there is always a corresponding lack of loving about the sufferer.

Sometimes it is a lack of loving response to other people, to family, friends, circumstances and organisations, a job or opportunity in life. Or perhaps tied in with this is a deeper dislike of the self, a feeling of worthlessness and failure, of guilt or distrust of our own motives.

Recently, a friend of ours told of an acquaintance who had taken to the practice of using a technique in which one chants and affirms the material things needed in life — and it appeared to be working (which it does), for she was gradually acquiring that which she sought. First a new flat, and then a new car, and so on.

Our friend indicated that she found this difficult to accept because she had been brought up to believe that it is wrong to ask for things for herself. It was selfish and perhaps even greedy so to do, she felt. But so long as the motive is of a pure kind, so long as we seek only good for ourselves and for others, and ask not for that which others already have and need, then this is truly man's right and heritage. It is a part of loving oneself. Not as a hedonistic narcissus, but as one who realises that there is actually plenty for all and you do not have to gain at another's expense. There is plenty to go around and because one man is poor, it is not necessary for you to share the experience with him, but you must be prepared to help him share your abundant experience if he so wishes!

This is as true of physical health or wholeness, as it is with wealth or supply, and with happiness. Our earth is capable of sustaining us all in a healthy, happy, and prosperous state. And there is no need, or indeed no point, to experience ill-health because of the physical problems of another — no need to "suffer with them" as it were. It is far more use for someone who is unwell to experience healthy, loving support and encouragement, than for them to see those around also being dragged (or induced) to ill-health too.

When her father was very ill, someone close to me once said, "If he takes me with him, well, so be it". She had recently been unwell with cancer, and had regained her health, but she was now neglecting herself almost to the point of martyrdom, in her attempts to "help" her father, although there was open resistance on his part to much of which she sought to do for him. He eventually passed on, quietly and peacefully in hospital. Five weeks later she followed him, leaving a devoted husband, three loving children and three young grandchildren.

Whilst it is right, of course, that we serve others; whilst it is our duty to put the needs of others as a priority, it is equally important for us to realise that certain impulses have motives of a doubtful character, and may even be a little masochistic. Many will perhaps quote "laying down his life for his friends", and the like, but a life of service is rather different from one of unnecessary, self-inflicted sorrow and pain. That helps no one. Someone who cares for others can only help them whilst he is also caring for himself. A doctor who is always ill, is no use to his patients.

It is increasingly evident to me that man was intended to live happily and prosperously, enjoying good physical and mental health. This is the only sense in creation for me and anything else is essentially perverse and "out of the flow" with all things and all life. Sometimes things go wrong, and it is not always easy to understand why, since the reasons can be complex and hidden by the sufferer, albeit at an unconscious level. But man's instinct is to seek health and happiness, for himself and his world, and, despite aberrations and set-backs, I believe he is slowly getting there.

One of the fondest memories of my childhood, is that of sitting out in a meadow, on a lazy, sunny afternoon, enjoying the wonderful feelings of well-being and peace that those days bring. I recall searching for those elusive four-leaf clovers, and the excitement when we thought we had found one. Looking at the carpet of white daisies, we would pick a few of these lovely gentle flowers to take home for mum to place in a jamjar of water, so that she could share some of our daytime reverie.

This image was cruelly jarred recently, when I saw a photograph of a mutated daisy someone had found in their garden. The flower was long, flat and grotesquely misshapen and had a bizarre, almost frightening appearance. An expert had advised that it was nothing to worry about, but merely the consequence of a garden spray, probably high in hormone based chemicals!

I was so worried by this. Indeed the sight of this flower horrified me. What are we doing to the creative flow of nature? What are we doing to our world? Is it surprising that we experience mysterious, distressing diseases in our bodies, or that we see others suffer for no apparent reason?

If we truly loved ourselves, we would then love others. We would be able to see the good in all situations, and dismiss the selfish and unloving. If we wish for life to go on, and for our children and their children to experience the joy of disease-free and pain-free lives; if we are serious in our quest for health, then it is only through loving ourselves and others, and consequently our world, that we will stop promoting harm, and instead pursue that road which leads gently and beautifully to that unshackled state called health.

I believe that all the good things in life are essentially inexpensive and simple. We tend to overcomplicate life in the name of progress, yet it is often the case that we have questionable motives and cease to respect both our true needs, and the needs of others.

Owning an expensive new car can be a pleasurable experience. It is fun to see the new gadgetry that man's ingenuity has provided, and a joy to have a comfortable, trouble free trip. But so often this simply leads on to spiralling desire for more and more extra features and trimmings, whilst the idea of a car as a vehicle for safe, comfortable and effective travel has become extremely remote, and the car has itself become something to admire and even worship, to the exclusion of so much else.

It is right that we enjoy our skills and their manifestation of discovery (or should it be re-discovery) as man's knowledge grows, but as the motives behind the creation of new things change, so does our relationship with the things we create. From the aids we devise and build to help us be more loving, capable and understanding, grow the objects of modern idolatry which tend to exclude a balanced perspective and growth, and we are set on a Path which takes us away from ourselves, from an understanding of who we are, to a point where we are subservient to that which we have created. We begin to love those things more than life itself, and this is where the rot sets in.

I know many who have far better relationships with their cars and hi-fi's than they do with their fellow man. There is no aeroplane, however marvellous, that can match the masterful dynamics of garden sparrows. There is no manu-factured perfume to compare with the delicate and gentle fragrance of healthy, natural woodland bluebells on a summers' day.

In loving ourselves and our fellowman, we begin to love that which our world can give to us, freely and lovingly, appreciating more and more of those things we take for granted, and that we usually fail to notice and hardly understand.

I always think it sad that many young children can relate in detail, the trite, and often violent content of the T.V. cartoons they are hypnotised by daily, yet they could not name or discuss in any meaningful way the flowers that grow in their own back garden. What are we doing to them? If we genuinely love our children and seek a contented, balanced life for them, then surely we must help them to understand and love the world in which they live, and which, after all, supports their material life.

In much of our medicine and current medical practice, we all too often witness a drug and technology orientated approach to healing our bodies and our minds, which is sadly found wanting. It tends to ignore the very qualities in man which give him life. Invasive techniques often half-kill the patient's will to live, destroying the life giving qualities his body was meant to employ in survival and regeneration. If only we could spend as much time and energy in helping to rid our world of pollutants that mutate and kill; if only we could spend time talking and listening to each other, enabling fears and anxieties to surface and be dealt with in a loving, caring fashion, so much suffering would be dissipated before it is allowed to damage and destroy.

I remember giving a talk to some trainee G.P.s at a local hospital. These young people were still full of idealism, yet it had been sadly bruised by a system of practice that had them both puzzled, and questioning. One young doctor expressed his frustration at the inadequate amount of time he could give to each patient, unable to offer more than 10 minutes per patient, in a general surgery. Instead of becoming a caring, loving healer, the system was making him a diagnostic bureaucrat, with little hope of effecting and enabling true cures and healings. Most patients would get better by themselves (or little worse), and others would have to be "referred elsewhere". Is it surprising that someone interviewed and treated in haste by a busy, over-worked G.P., may then be on the slippery slope of despair, as symptoms are suppressed and the inner unhappiness is either dismissed or ignored, until it surfaces at a later date, often more dramatically and more dangerously? The self-image is battered once more and we sometimes never completely recover.

My intention is certainly not to criticize medical Doctors, and those engaged in orthodox medical practice. Life threatening and serious complaints need all the help they can obtain. But I do mean help of a positive, loving kind that puts the patient first, and I do mean ALL. There are many simple, effective, life changing approaches that can certainly complement all other forms of treatment, without harm or conflict and they will support a sick person from his essence at his creative centre, from where true regeneration and well-being spring.

More important still, a loving and caring approach to life and to oneself, is the best preventative I know in the maintenance of good health.

Some time ago I heard a song my daughter had learned at school and had come home singing one afternoon. It had a beautiful lilt to it, and its message is so wonderful.

"Love is something if you give it away,
　　　　　　　　give it away,
　　　　　　　　give it away,
Love is something if you give it away.
You end up having more.
It's just like a magic penny,
Hold it close and you won't have any.
Lend it, spend it,
You'll have so many
They'll roll all over the floor!"

My intention is simple. Through these pages I offer ideas,

observations and truths which, if applied in daily life, will help the reader to become a more loving, caring, thoughtful (positive that is) and consequently healthy person.

We may all have known those who have become seriously ill and yet who display an apparently loving and kind disposition. Many involved in the treatment of cancer in particular will be able to cite so many cases where this is so.

However, there can be little doubt that, at some level of their consciousness, they have perhaps been wounded by events in life to such an extent, that they no longer express the joy of living through their own affairs and actions, and feel that life has nothing left for them to give to it. They no longer completely love themselves, or their world. And sometimes, even the love they express for others has become tired and jaded.

I invite you to follow me through my ideas, the things I have had to use for myself and others. I claim no originality, only that truth is faith. Our discoveries already exist, waiting for us to find and recognise them. All the great teachings are based upon love of the self, through love of one's fellow man.

The truth is, "Being loving, is being healthy".

PART 1

"IT'S THE LOVING THINGS YOU SAY"

When I was a schoolteacher, I spent some time working with young disadvantaged children. It was hard, though often rewarding work, and children have that disarming, direct quality in their relationships that we somehow lose, because we become tactful or deceitful (whichever you prefer) as we become older, and more worldweary.

One little boy, who had several physical problems and an unhappy homelife, came up to me at the end of one Christmas term, whilst we were removing the paper decorations we had used for our party. He gently held my arm, and looked into my eyes and said, "Sir, I love you. I wish I could come home with you".

The words touched something deep inside me, and opened a door to a world of feeling that I had forgotten was there. The power of his words, giving life and energy to his thoughts, had a profound effect upon me from then onwards, and provided a memory I cherish.

When words are coloured with true feeling they do more than simply sound as a vibration. They give to that sound a quality that affects us at every level of our being, spiritually, mentally, emotionally and physically. If we are surrounded by words of love, we grow accordingly. Some feel the example of the cursing of the fig tree by Jesus is just to demonstrate that power, albeit in a more negative vein.

Of course, it is important to remember that we are on the receiving end of all the words we say, as well as hear. People who speak in uncharitable and harmful ways begin to reflect their words. They take on a vibration of increasing negativity and, in time, this begins to be outpictured in their lives.

First it shows in demeanour and physical expression and in the clothes and colours they choose. Next, they begin to attract people of similar type into their lives — the "birds of a feather" syndrome, like attracting like. This ultimately manifests as disease in their minds and bodies as the true creative flow within them is jammed by "bad signals" and a morbid condition appears in the physical body.

The subconscious mind has no sense of humour, so watch your words. "Many a true word spoken in jest" is a great teaching to be observed by all. You record everything you say, only for it to surface later with all the come-back that it will attract into your life.

There are two ways in which we can change our lives, centering upon our spoken words. We must first look at what we say about ourselves and how we can bring power into our lives, and mend our dented halos, and we can transform the lives of those around us by the words we sent in their directions.

A former patient of mine always complained that few people bothered to telephone her, and that she was frequently on her own. I pointed out to her that her conversation on the telephone was always concerned with her health problems and how little money she had. She had so little love for herself, that she attracted these things into her life, and consequently her words brought about her reality. She became what she said — lonely, short of money and in poor health. Nobody appeared to love her, for she appeared not to love herself.

I remember in my youth, how one or two people would joke about my lack of height, and ultimately, I allowed this to influence how I saw myself. Instead of being proud of what God had given me, I was embarrassed by the spoken view of another until I saw myself as a funny little chap, prone to being overweight! The damage had been done — I felt being small was a crime and overweight was the norm for me. A life-time battle had commenced. I really didn't like my physical self at all, and yet, I was truly a remarkable being. Within me there were organs and biological functions of the most mind boggling complexity and durability, working away beautifully and reliably. They were so superior to anything man had constructed. My whole body was a testimony to the power of growth in love, yet I had allowed the negative words of others to influence that inner vision of myself, which eventually determines what I am, both mentally and physically.

A medical acquaintance told me that even in a body ravaged with cancer, most of it is functioning surprisingly well, even at the point of death. So it is imperative at all times to recognise how remarkable we are and what incredible potential each of us has. We are all different, with differing strengths and qualities. But we all have an enormous capacity to express love about and through ourselves, especially through our words. Words can influence our thoughts, and the thoughts of others.

Can you recall making a judgement about a person because you disliked their physical appearance, yet upon their speaking to you, having that image transformed as they radiated? This demonstrates one power of our words, words can transform. A happy man attracts happy friends and circumstances. A loving man is loved.

One of the most important changes we can make is to start loving our bodies. Now, O.K. like me, you may not be just what the mail-order catalogue requires, *but most of us aren't!* We were meant to be different, and even a malfunctioning organ or limb is still doing a remarkable job, and it can only improve its service to us when being loved. Condemnation and insult won't help at all.

Make this a daily routine. Upon waking each day, you should lovingly commission your body for the day's work. It should be washed and cleansed. During your sleep period there has been much regeneration of tissue, so you should cleanse off the dead tissue, both inside and out, before you do anything else. It makes me shudder to think that many start the day with a cigarette and a cup of tea. Would you try to impress a new girl or boyfriend by blowing harmful fumes over them and then spraying them with poisonous chemicals? You are going to have a new loving relationship with your body, so cleanse it both outside and inside with filtered or boiled water before you do anything else.

Then take a few minutes to sit quietly and express these

thoughts to your body. Your body will be listening so say it aloud. Even if you feel a little embarrassed at first, that will pass. And anyway, it is your life and your body, and ultimately only you can look after it properly.

> "From head to toe
> My body is filled with love.
> From my head to my toes
> I have my body working for me.
> Love circulates throughout me from my heart,
> ever flowing,
> Warming and caressing every tissue,
> every fibre and cell in my body.
> All the organs of my body are working
> so well for me.
> I am filled with health giving love.
> My body is fed and cleansed beautifully,
> as the creative breath of life fills me,
> renewing and restoring.
> I thank and bless my body with love
> From my head to my toes."

You must begin to work at praising your body, and not condemning it IN ANY WAY. A friend was always saying, "My eyes are always giving me problems" and, of course, they did. Refer to your body, only in a positive fashion. If, like I did, you refer to others as a negative bodily function, then you had better stop at once and reprogramme your attitudes and words. I had many " 'pains' in my neck", some quite severe and of considerable duration!

Treat your body with love and give it plenty of encouragement. No child ever learned anything worthwhile from continual scolding. Speaking with a loving authority about yourself is the first step in gaining truly good health of mind and body. Everything in creation strives for perfection and that includes you! Why should you impede yourself when there are plenty of others trying to do it for you? Negative types attract one another, and you are seeking to express only love, and thus link with the positive things in life, which include good health.

I am sure you can recall occasions when you have tried really hard to perform a particular task and, believing you have done well, you have been shattered and hurt by another's sarcastic or negative comments. Instead of helping you to grow, they have put you down. If you can recall how you felt, it is exactly the same for your body when you are negative and hurtful about what it seeks to achieve for you! There is nothing wrong in seeking good things for you. Remember, you can only help others when you can help yourself, and what is truly good for you, brings good to others.

One patient of mine once expressed her realization that her ill health was largely the result of neglecting her own interests, pursuits and well-being, for the love of her family. Now her poor health was bringing difficulty into everyone's lives, not only her life, but also those of her husband and two daughters. The key to the improvement in her health was linked very much to her change in attitude. She started to love herself. We are what we think we are, and we should say only what we think we should be.

Another important area of statement and self criticism is the "I can't" syndrome, when "I can't" really means "I won't". We are often made to feel that we can't do this or that, simply because others impose their judgements upon us, and belittle our efforts. Instead of loving us for what we are and our attempts at self-improvement, they criticise us, seeking to deny our right to growth. Life is about growth. In many respects the journey is more important than the arrival. It is often the most interesting part, and we would never get anywhere without travelling.

If your "I can't" really means "I won't", and if your "I won't" really says "I'm afraid to try", then your love of yourself is seriously lacking and harmed by your fear of failure. Your subconscious mind has been filled with negative rubbish, and this must be disposed of, very quickly. And, since nature abhors a vacuum, you must replace it with good, positive ideas. You wouldn't deliberately hurt anyone you truly loved, would you? This is as true of yourself as it is of others. There is no challenge given to you in life that you cannot deal with. There is no circumstance in your life that you cannot change for the better. There is ALWAYS something you can do. Just think about that for a moment. Whatever the situation, there is ALWAYS something you can do.

Let's start off in the way we mean to continue by stopping the "I can't". Just sit down quietly and consider this statement:-

"There is one creative power in the Universe. It is a loving, creative, good power that builds the perfect ideas of form and shape and colour. It creates the flowers and trees, the birds and animals. It is only man's negative attitudes and actions that bring deformity. I am part of this perfect, creative, loving power. I can achieve all I need to achieve in my life."

I ask you not to start "I can't" or "I won't" or "I am not" about this statement. This statement is true. It is about you and your essence. We live on a planet designed for love, and when that love is allowed to flow, all things for good become possible. I ask you to read that statement to yourself, out loud, several times. Just allow the words to sink in and let yourself identify with them. In this book I ask you to make no judgements except that you try what I ask you to do. It is in the eating that the proof of the pudding lies. Any theory has only the power of its application and success. All else is illusion.

We all know that a young child has the ability to walk. But he has to learn the technique, gain the confidence, grow the muscles and experience the desire to walk. You desire to be healthy or you would not have started to read this book. To learn (or re-learn) to love yourself you have to exercise your spiritual muscles and get them used to the idea of the new way you choose to go. They can do it for you, they have simply been programmed the other way for such a long time, that there is a little cramp in them. They'll be fine, given gentle, regular exercise, and you will feel so much better for it.

One lady who came to me for help had been using tranquilisers for many, many years, and had become dependent upon them. Her self-image was badly battered, and she had little confidence in her own ability to cope with her life. We had begun a gentle programme of treatment to help her to cope with withdrawal symptoms, and bring about the tranquil state of mind that the drugs had failed to effect.

When in a state of deep relaxation I gave her the simple statement, "I am doing so well". I repeated the statement to her several times and then asked her to do likewise. In the ensuing weeks this statement was central to her recovery and improvement. It simply reminded her of her own power, of how much she could do if only she gave herself a little credit and a little love. In the words of a song I once heard — "a little loving goes a long, long, long, long way", and she had begun to love herself.

Isn't there a danger of becoming an ego centred, self-seeking bore? Well, at present I am helping you to begin anew the way in which you view yourself and your capabilities, and how you can use that loving power to create health in your mind and body. This is not for the ears of others at present. It is for you. Get yourself right then you will be right for others!

Keep your self-improvement to yourself. Others will inevitably notice a difference in you when you become more loving, because you will change, for change you must, after all you want to be more healthy, and it is your current attitudes that have made you as they are. So be prepared for changes at every level. As you begin to say only those things that you CAN do. As you begin to speak lovingly of yourself and your body, you will appear different to others. Your body will begin to change as will your palate and even your taste in clothes, cosmetics, and so on. You are beginning a new way of living and being, but, for the time being, keep it to yourself. Don't give others the opportunity to put negativity into your good ideas and words. If others inquire as to what you are doing, you can simply tell them that you find your life is changing in loving positive little ways, and leave it at that.

So often, speaking of some good idea or project meets with the disapproval or doubts of others. They begin to judge what you seek to do from THEIR viewpoint. Because they don't love themselves very much, they feel you must be the same and try to influence your life — and they have no right to do that; they have no right to make their weakness your weakness, so, for the time being, don't give them the opportunity; keep the power where it is needed, in the situation of loving yourself. Speak the idea only to yourself. You will discover loving ways of helping them later.

This statement is a very powerful one, and many of those I help have found it useful. Write it down and use it.

"I express only love. I speak love of myself and my affairs. I give good creative worth to all that I tackle. In shortchanging a task or action, I shortchange myself. I see only love, and I express only love. I speak only love for I love life, and I am life."

Repeated several times, daily for a week, this will have an effect upon you of the most profound and positive kind. Believe nothing until you've tried it — so all I ask is that you try it!

"But I don't express, or even feel like expressing love!" O.K., but recall when perhaps you have felt quite unlike laughing, even quite miserable maybe, but a chance remark, a phrase, sentence or comment has brought a smile to your face. All changed in a moment. Some chord was struck and you began to *feel* different, yet it was only a word, after all.

Many a good comedian relies on the use of words to transform his audience from a quiet, or even hostile one, to one rippling with laughter. How that audience was transformed simply by words that were carefully chosen and used.

Well, you will use the same dynamic in your life. Your

mind and body may resist this spiritual upsurge at first. After all, it has been conditioned to be unloving. But now is your chance. Gradually creep up unawares, and say those carefully chosen words until they strike a chord — then they will become more than words. They will become the instigators of the most positive change you will ever make in your life. Most informed thought now tends to accept that our world is largely of our own making and that what we think is what we get — "as a man thinketh in his heart, so he is" — but our thoughts are conditioned by our speech and a man who is rich in speech is rich in consciousness, and therefore, rich in life.

It follows that a man who is loving and healthy in his words, is loving and healthy in his mind, body and affairs. The complexities of modern life have, unfortunately, taken us away from our simple understanding of spiritual man, and the way we can invoke the good, loving power in our lives. It is simple but it requires persistence and faith, a faith through knowledge. The knowledge that all good things for us already exist. The knowledge that we were meant to be happy, healthy and prosperous beings, loving ourselves and loving life. And with a little application we can get back into this flow.

It is imperative to start the day with a positive, creative, loving statement. The first words of your day are crucial and they truly determine the nature of your day. By expressing creative thoughts about yourself you align yourself with all good, loving opportunities. Instead of seeing the negative, you will see the positive in events and circumstances. One man's clump of weeds is another's haven of natural wild flowers.

Attitudes transform your day, and your life. You are like a magnet so make sure you get the current to go into the right direction.

In the morning, after commissioning your body from "Head to Toe", use the statement, "I start my day with love. Today is a day of opportunity for me. All good things will come my way. I deserve them and say thank you." See the changes that occur!

The expressing of gratitude is a marvellous way of expressing love. Saying "thank-you" is a powerful thing to do. It signifies your acceptance of your good, and so aligns you with those things you seek, bringing them closer and closer to manifestation in and around you.

Gratitude is also linked to praise. Saying "well-done" to your mind and body for what is achieved in your day is very important, for it re-inforces in your consciousness, the direction you wish to take in your life as you follow a new pathway.

One of the first techniques a student teacher learns is that of profuse praise and congratulation when a pupil achieves, however small that achievement might appear. Properly nurtured, such an experience of praise will be the first of many for the pupil, as he strives towards greater and more impressive goals.

"Beauty is in the eye of the beholder," in other words, it is a subjective experience. The same is true of achievement. We all have areas in our lives where we have to work harder than others. Some things come easier than others, so it is important, ALWAYS, to praise and congratulate so that the warm glow inside is continually kindled as we build success upon success. We have to build an expectance into our lives. It is not enough to want or desire; it is not enough to believe but rather we have to expect things to occur, so that they become part of our reality, part of our consciousness.

My wife has a cousin who is a very successful business man. It doesn't seem to matter what area of activity he engages in, he always meets with great success. The outstanding reason for this, is his level of expectance. He entertains no idea of failure, but he only works towards success and expects it. If something is not happening he does not allow himself to wallow in a sense of inadequacy or despair, but he builds into the experience the idea that things will turn for the better, and this is then demonstrated by words and actions. He will never engage in a conversation of failure. He desires, believes and expects success. Many people don't, even though they pretend they do, and they continually speak of limitations, difficulty, problems and so on.

You must build the expectance of health, wealth and happiness into your life by congratulating yourself for your achievements and successes. At the end of each day, make a list of successes. It may be making a cake, or mowing the lawn. It may be financial success or promotion. It may be doing something which you have been afraid to do. Whatever it is, the important thing is to write it down and then read it out to yourself, loud and clear, followed by a "well-done", adding your name afterwards.

I remember once, a woman praising her husband for successfully paying the last of 24 hire purchase instalments, on his car. For a man, as he was, who had always had difficulty in managing money, this was truly an achievement and his good wife knew this. She also knew a thing or two about love.

Make a habit of congratulating yourself. There is nothing wrong with a habit, so long as it is a good one. Make a fuss of yourself, be proud of who you are, and fill yourself with a loving feeling of selfworth.

Do "voice", or say, the achievements and the "well-dones". Your mind will become accustomed to success for your good, and do all it can to achieve more and more.

This applies equally to your body. Nature tends to emulate, and if you praise the body for working well, any negative or diseased condition will immediately begin to feel out of place. The vibrations of praise and loving that your words produce, will be alien to disease and it feels an instinct to change, to fit in with the pattern you are creating, the new creative, loving and healthy you.

Give no truck to negative thoughts and unloving words. They simply stop the flow of life.

Anyone who doubts the power of loving words need only recall the words of the man who drove his car into the rear of another. As the angry third party jumped out of his car to attack him, he simply smiled and said, "Please forgive me, I am so very sorry for what I have done, it was entirely my fault". This dissipated the hostility at once and the situation resolved in an amicable and happy way.

When we seek to experience something for our good, we have to convert our desire and belief into confident expectancy. It is absolutely no use wishing and hoping, and believing in possibilities. We have to cultivate a "loving expectancy" linked to a sense of our deserving the best, for that is truly so. This is why it is sometimes imperative to say "thank you" in advance. It seems strange to those of us brought up with the idea that expecting things for ourselves is wrong. That to think in such a way is tantamount to greed. But for most of us, this ridiculous attitude is simply another nail in the coffin of self-worth and a denial of our right to health and happiness. It is very much geared to the idea that a little suffering is good for the soul, and it is responsible for so many complexes and sorrows in man's nature, that it has led to many sadomasochistic practices in the name of religion in particular, which are abominable.

Of course, sometimes we have to get by without a certain thing, but simply, because it is inappropriate and unnecessary to our life at that time. That is never, never an excuse for poor health and poverty. These are conditions of the mind and man's consciousness, and only you can eradicate them for yourself, but eradicate them you really can. And you start by loving yourself, and the excellent qualities with which you are endowed, and blessed.

"What do I do to create this confident expectancy?" You will notice that all the statements and affirmations that I ask you to use are structured to assume that things are both happening, and have already happened. They are positive, and will give thanks for that which has already happened, even though we may feel and think that all is still the same in our bodies. We have to realise some important truths, here and now.

First, perfection already exists in our world. In any given circumstance, perfection already exists. All we have to do is REALIZE it so.

I know that you may raise some objections — "my back

still hurts, my leg is still bruised" etc., and so on and so on. But the truth is that our world, our universe, was created perfect, without blemish, without disease, perfect and whole. Through his ignorance, man has increasingly moved away from this perfect pattern that exists, and hence his reality is merely a shadow of the real.

For a moment, I simply ask you to suspend any judgement and listen to what I say. If you disagree, then that is your choice and your right. But what I suggest will not harm and hurt you. It will only do you good so when you do make a judgement, I ask you to do so with that in mind and that you will only properly evaluate these ideas by trying them. The proof is in the eating! And this is not a new idea. It is the basis of all the major religions and philosophies in recorded history.

For all creation, there exists a perfect pattern, rather like a mould, which we can fill with energy and matter, to manifest form and shape. As far as our bodies are concerned, this creative flow of energy is filtered by our mind, where our thoughts dwell.

Now we know that there is no such thing as a solid, and that all matter is made from lots and lots of tiny particles, darting to and fro at different speeds and frequencies, in a multitude of directions.

Nothing is solid.

Look at the fingers of your hand. That they appear solid is purely an illusion if you like, or a limit in your "seeing" or perception. Look at one finger carefully. Study it a little and then gently tap this book with it. A gentle noise will be heard, a sound which, as science has also (re) discovered, is simply a mass of vibrations.

This finger of yours, and in fact your whole body, is simply a wonderful, intricate web of vibrations, held together in a pattern by your subconscious MIND. Your subconscious MIND is identifying the frequencies and rhythms at which its home (for that is what your body truly is) should pulse, and vibrate. Your subconscious mind recognises the pattern, and links with it, to express your physical form — the YOU we all see! This makes you even more remarkable than perhaps you had ever thought and conceived possible before. You are the governor of a remarkable Empire, with all the awe-inspiring responsibilities that entails, and all the incredible possibilities it offers to you. Your mind controls your body, and you can control and re-programme your mind.

Your commands are more than just the simple words that they at first appear. They contain the power to alter the vibrations and frequencies in your body, your "Empire", in the most incredible and loving ways. Your influence is immense. You can take your body away from that negative, diseased image. You can rub out the mistakes in your pattern which are allowing disease to occur, and you can replace them with loving, perfect, guidelines for them to follow until the whole, beautiful you manifests. By giving out positive, loving vibrations, you become a positive loving being — you cannot become anything else.

The vibrations in your voice (words and sounds) as you can now see, will have a direct and profound effect upon your physical body. The easiest thing for you to do, is to bring back into line with the perfect pattern for you, all those atoms and minute particles, buzzing around, seeking to create the shape and form that you direct to them.

So you must be truly careful what you say from now on, both to yourself and to others, for you can see how it is possible for you to influence their vibrations a little too! (It is quite surprising how children often appear physically, just how their parents see them in their imagination, and speak of them). Thus, the spoken and sung word is all important. It can, and will be responsible for keeping you (or not) in tune with the perfect self for you.

If you think for a moment of two types of building, an old church or place of worship, and a prison or place of torture. In most places of true worship you will sense the peace and lovingness, echoed by those who frequent it, for the building will be imbued with such feelings. In a prison, however caring the staff may be, you will sense the sorrow, the anger, the frustrations and fears of its inmates. In one, people mostly sing songs and say prayers of praise and hope, of love and peace, whilst in the other the dominant conversation will be of despair, regret, and a whole plethora of negative ideas. I feel certain that most people, taken blindfold into the buildings as described above, will be able easily to discern one from another, and identify which is which. If we can do this to a building we visit once or twice a week or where perhaps we spend just a few years, what can we do to the body, our temple, which we inhabit each and every moment for our whole life!

I hope by now that it is becoming clear that our spoken word is so very, very powerful and that, to start with at least, we have got to work hard at re-programming and re-aligning our mental and physical senses through the power of our words. Remember, the proof is in the eating, so you must give yourself a really good introduction to speaking in a loving, positive and creative fashion. You may be clearing away years of dross and so it will perhaps take a little time, but you will, truly, see changes at a fairly early stage. You will notice people beginning to react to you in a different manner.

I remember one patient saying to me how he seemed to be meeting a more pleasant and caring type of person, without making any conscious attempt to do so on his part. Even shop assistants seemed more friendly and happier when he approached them. Quite simply, he was changing profoundly his words, his countenance and his bearing. He was enjoying a new way of being, and those he met were increasingly aware of these qualities, since they truly "rub-off" and influence others. Consequently he attracted those very qualities to him — there was little room for anything else to exist.

So, to recap, you must change the way you speak of yourself from the negative to the positive, from the detrimental to the loving. You must make certain types of words and phrases the norm in your vocabulary so that any "rogues" that creep in will be out of place, soon to be corrected or rejected. You must allow and encourage the change in attitude to yourself to flow out to others as you speak positively and lovingly to them, and about them.

No sound ever dies. It flows on forever out through the ether, onwards into the Cosmos. Start filling it with love. It really is simple.

As I said earlier when we talk too much about a situation we tend to take the power out of it, at least we allow others so to do. So use a degree of economy in your speech for whilst we should never be mean, a spendthrift is always falling short. Don't become a chatterbox, but rather give off a flow of beauty and love, in pure vibration.

PART 2

SEEKING AND IDENTIFYING
THE POSITIVE

Take a small pocket book and begin a list of all the things that you do in your day. Start on a Monday, if you can, and write down all the good things that you can, and do effect during that day. It doesn't matter how small or insignificant they may appear, write them down. Your list may read "drove the car to work", "answered post", "held interviews" etc or "got breakfast", "dressed children", "packed luncheons", and so on.

Write it down. Do it methodically, every day, as soon as you have done something that helps you, or others, put it on your list, either at home or at work, for yourself or for others.

Keep the pocket book with you all day, and sometime during the evening, read through your list. Even allowing for omissions and inevitables, you will be both staggered, surprised and pleased with what you can and do achieve in a day, even a seemingly uneventful one. You must include things such as "holding a door open for customers", "changing a nappy ($\times$ 20!)" or perhaps "wrote cheerful note to friend". These are all positive, loving things that you must recognise in yourself for they are of immense importance. They tell a story about you. They start to build a picture of who you really are, your true self. The true creative loving you.

You will notice that I have not included any apparent failures or negative events or occurrences.

The reason for this is simple.

Sometimes, in order to start the car we have to turn the key in the ignition several times, before the engine starts to run smoothly. These little attempts are important steps in reaching a goal yet at the same time they seem like failures but they are not. It is the memory of the ignition firing properly we wish to keep. Similarly, we need to understand that a negative statement or action is not truly us. When we behave in such a way we are not really showing what we can do at all, but we are seeing our frustrations and fears as they shut out our potential to be positive beings, within the loving creative flow of life. It is our ability to be so, that we must record, remember and respect.

Now back to your pocket book.

When you identify how many things you both can do and have done, sit quietly for a few moments and re-live some of the best moments of your day.

In your mind's eye, see yourself doing whatever you have selected, as vividly and clearly as you possibly can. Repeat this several times and be sure to see yourself clearly, enjoying what you are doing.

You may find this technique a little difficult at first, some do. But eventually you will become masterful at it, and enjoy re-living positive events from your day.

One housebound lady frequently used the image of herself stroking her dog whilst she planned the evening meal for her family. It was something she enjoyed doing and that she did so well, even with the challenge of her physical handicap.

When you have finished with your image, read the following statement to yourself.

"I bless the day I have been given. I am thankful for the things I have accomplished, in a good, loving and perfect way".

Say it three times and then sit quietly for a minute or two, allowing the feeling to flow within you.

You will feel good. You will feel happy. And you will feel loving toward yourself, and pleased with what you can do.

On days of a particular achievement it is even more important to follow this procedure. The flow of loving power that you will feel, will be immense at such a time, and it can be channelled and used for your further good, and for the good of others.

Carry this procedure through for a week and don't worry

should you repeat something many times in your list. Your
mind will know what is important for you to remember of
these positive events. As the week continues, the things you
write down will begin to change as you begin to change, but
don't worry about that for now. Simply be prepared for it.
You will notice yourself more closely as time goes by and
consequently what you consider unimportant now, will
become important, and viceversa. So just do as I suggest.
When you have reached Friday night, look through the
whole week.

However humdrum you feel your life is, and however
boring or useless you have considered yourself in the past,
you will be positively surprised at how much you can and do
achieve in your day to day living and your image of yourself
will be changing for the better, slowly but surely.

And, as this happens, so will you also be changing for the
better, becoming more positive, more aware of your
potential and much more inclined to love yourself for the
good qualities you have and express. Well done!

Take a break for a couple of days from your list, but be
sure to repeat the words I have given you at a quiet time
towards the end of your day. Cultivate this as a habit either
on its own, or tacked on to any other prayer and/or
meditative time you would normally keep. Be proud of who
you are and of what you have already achieved in your life.
Think on those things and then add the things, the myriad of
things that you know you will achieve, even though you
cannot, at present, even begin to forsee what they might be,
just rest assured that they will be many.

During your next week, commence on the Monday with a
new pocket book if you can. Use the same approach to your
day as before but this time, instead of writing down what
you do each day, make a note of what is done for you by
others in a positive, loving way. Use the same principles as
before. View the apparently negative, or "failings" for what
they really are — incomplete and distorted expressions of
true life. Record the good things, the smiles, the warm
handshakes, the offers of help, the acts of kindness, the

prepared meals, the ironed shirts, the repaired watch, the
encouraging words. They are all done especially for you.
Granted, in some instances the deed will be "paid for" as a
service. But every man is worthy of his hire, and a good
service is always worth many many times over, the price we
pay. I can think of one young bank teller who always smiles
and greets customers in such a beautiful, loving and friendly
way. She is worth a king's ransom to a weary shopper
seeking to make a transaction on a busy, cold day.

Write them all down, all those good things done for you.

Don't forget those bottles of milk left each day, without
fail, whatever the weather, and the mail arriving on your
doormat, often having travelled through many hands, over
many miles to reach you remarkably quickly most days.

As before, toward the end of each day, take a few
moments to look through your list of things done for you,
services rendered, courtesies, encouragements, and so on.
Just take note of them and then, in the quiet of your mind,
recall the best and most enjoyable events of your day.
Remember as much about them as you can, the colours, the
perfumes, the sounds that help you recall clearly — enjoy
them all, and then, when you have finished the sequence of
images and memories, read the following statement to
yourself:-

"I recognise and give thanks for these things done for me
this day. I see in them the true flow of creative love,
expressing as service to me. I know that more and more
good things will happen for me tomorrow, and each new
day in perfect, loving ways".

Say this three times then be still, as before, for a few
minutes. You will feel the loving flow within you, moving
once more. It will start as a physical sensation around your
solar plexus (stomach area) and spread onwards through the
rest of your body. Enjoy it and give thanks for it, for you are
truly becoming a positive, loving person.

There is a dynamic here, a "power-flow" which is important
to recognise. You are training yourself to do two things.

First to have only positive, loving thoughts and actions for others, and secondly to recognise these qualities in those you meet in your day. This, done regularly, will change your life and your world. You are developing new habits, the most positive, loving habits it is possible to express, and you will become those habits.

You are also seeing only the good in other people and eventually, more and more, you will experience such events and people in your life.

Your positive reaction to others will also help them to grow, as they too will *feel* different in your presence and will seek to be more like the new you. In fact, you are starting a revolution, so be prepared for the changes for they will surely manifest your life.

TOWARD POSITIVE HEALTH

Disease is dis-ease. When we are ill, we, to all intents and purposes, demonstrate a willingness to be un-loving. We show that we are basically unhappy with ourselves and our life. In fact, we are saying that we no longer love ourselves and our world.

There are two things to remember at this point. First, we create the conditions of our physical body. One way or another, it is our attitude to our bodies that determines our state of health. Whatever we start with as we set out on life's journey, is either maintained or destroyed by our own attitudes; stifled and twisted by negative and distorted thoughts, words and images.

Secondly, perhaps more hard to take, is the fact that we shape our world. Our environment is of our making. Agreed, you are but one of many, but you are already learning simple, yet effective ways of changing yourself, and now it is time to realise that you can do the same to your world.

Have you ever noticed how some people never succeed with flowers and plants in their attempts at gardening? Somehow, the plants either die, or never really achieve

much, they never grow as lavishly as they do in the gardens
of others. The next time you walk around your neighbour-
hood, take time to study the gardens. Look at the layout of
the garden. The arrangement of the flowerbeds, the shrubs,
paving stones, the shape of the lawn. It will speak more
loudly and more clearly about he who tends it (or not as the
case may be) than any words could ever do.

I have a neighbour who is one of the most meticulous and
thorough of men. His neat, immaculate garden reflects that,
even to the blossoms on the plants he grows; they show an
incredible uniformity of shape and size, evenness of hue, and
clarity of design. The same plants in other gardens are
somehow less concise. Through your observations, you will
notice gardens, each attractive in their own way, perhaps
with similar plants yet expressing differing qualities. Some
lawns will be crisp and straight, uniformly green, with not a
weed in sight. Others will see grass mixed with clover and
buttercups, with a great variety of tones and shades of green
and perhaps shaped with curved edging, more flowing in
design.

Sadly, some will show neglect and even abuse. They will
be totally unloved!

Each garden, I assure you, will reflect the attitude of its
owner or custodian, to the world in which he lives and the
way in which he or she reflects the creative love of the
universe.

It was quite noticeable that at a time in my life when I had
not brought to completion any of my good ideas, when they
were not "flowering" if you like, that it was reflected in my
garden. Lots of green, in many, many shades, but few
flowers. Happily, this has changed and as I write this chapter
my garden is full of beautiful vibrant colourful blooms. They
have come into my consciousness as my life begins to flower
and bear its most precious fruit. We only receive that which
we give. It is reaping and sowing. Your garden is a perfect
harvest of your attitudes.

Today our world is facing a great challenge. Man simply
does not love his planet. He does not show sufficient caring

love for it, for if he did, he would not harm it in the manner that he does. He would not tear it apart, ceaselessly, bruising and scaring as he goes, if he truly cared for this planet earth.

He spends millions and millions of pounds each year on research into new drugs, medicines, and techniques in an attempt to cure the ravages of disease, and yet he gives proportionally little care to the place that is his home and from which all the components of his physical body have their genesis or beginning. He abuses the Mother which supplies the sustaining and regenerating minerals, gases and foods that keep him alive in the physical realm. And yet man will complain or feel cheated when he suffers disease, disease which is a direct consequence of his lack of care and love for his environment and his world.

The Chernobyl nuclear disaster has helped us all to realize, if we didn't realize it before, that we have created some potential monsters that could easily destroy us all and damage our world beyond repair.

Nobody knows what the long term effects will be of Chernobyl, but we have already seen contaminated sheep, who did nothing other than graze freely many thousands of miles away from the damaged nuclear reactor. And our masters tell us that the risk to health is minimal, if any exists at all. Who do they think they are deluding?

Without doubt, our current custom of a repair oriented health care system is ridiculous. Our attitudes have simply got to change. And this is where you are able to start to grow your loving of the world, and move to a positive loving state of health. If we each learn to love our small patch of the earth, that little piece more, then the whole world would take a massive step upwards.

Remember, your attitudes affect others profoundly. You are becoming increasingly powerful as you progress through this book. And as your power grows so does your responsibility to use your power with love and care.

Positive health is born of positive outlook. A positive outlook is not strident and uncaring, but reassuring and loving. This is exactly what you can become.

Take yourself off to a park or woodland, or perhaps your own garden or some natural spot. Anywhere where you can be a little quiet and be still for a while. If it is something new to you; or a departure from your normal behaviour, others may think you are behaving a little strange perhaps, but speak gently and think kindly and well of them, and they will leave you alone. These are important steps. You are becoming a new loving person, so enjoy it and persist with it. The prize is the greatest you can have in life.

Ensure you are somewhere near to either some flowers, or some foliage. During the winter time, you could sit near some plants in a greenhouse or conservatory, or you could find some shrubs, or alpines to be near. Whatever you do, just be near to some plants.

Settle close to a particular plant or shrub. Look at it very carefully. Gradually isolate it from the others around it. Observe the main features of the plant; its shape, its colour, its textures.

Notice the way in which it is, in itself, a multiplicity of shapes and patterns, all being linked together in the most incredible and wonderful ways. Continue to concentrate on the plant of your choice and then direct your attention to the base of the stem where it reaches out from the soil.

Imagine that you are there, standing at that point, aware only of that part of the garden. Be aware that the plant is continually drawing goodness to sustain it from the soil below, freely and easily, without any problem, and in sufficient quantity to keep it well and strong.

Next, allow your thoughts to travel up and around the plant, exploring each part and detail of every level as you do so. Move your attention around just as if you are on a relaxing journey visiting a new and wonderful landscape. Enjoy this experience for as many minutes as you wish.

When your attention has reached the top or flower of your plant, continue with your observations until you experience a feeling of completion, or that "I have arrived" sensation that we feel at the end of an enjoyable trip.

At this point, close your eyes for a few moments. Take a

deep breath through your nostrils and experience the flow of
energy from your chosen plant to you, as it enters your head,
gradually spreading and filling the whole of your body. Do
this several times until you feel perfumes and freshness of the
air have entirely "soaked" your physical body, and your
mind. Recall that the plant you observed is also being
sustained by the light of the sun (even if you cannot see it on a
particular day) in a free-giving and loving way. Uncondition-
ally, the sun gives its light to the plant as it does also to you.

It is here that you will begin to feel increasingly at one with
the plant on which you have focused, and also with the
whole of creation, in the sense of plants, flowers, trees, birds
and insects, animals and the elements.

You will be aware that you too, like the plants and flowers,
are a part of the loving earth which you share as home, and
you can more easily identify with the power of the light we
receive each day, to help us to live and grow. You and your
chosen plant are creations of that same environment which
gives you every opportunity you will ever need for health
and happiness. Suddenly the world will have changed and so
will your relationship to it.

You will feel much more a part of it and you will start to
identify with all the beautiful possibilities in your environment.

You will seek health and well-being for your world for
you will feel that you are both one. Its health will become
your health, and so whatever love you had for these things
before, will be increased seven fold, EACH TIME that you
follow the procedure I have outlined.

At first I suggest that you do this at least once every day.
Over a period of time you will find that this process will
become so natural to you, that you will be drawn into this
communion with nature at odd moments throughout your
daily life, so much so, that you will become inseparable from
your natural environment and you will always feel a part of
it. Your consciousness will be imbued with its gentle power
and love and you will never lose it again.

Many experiences will open for you here. First and
foremost, you will benefit from the healing power of the

plants and flowers you link with. Plants give out emanations, gases, perfumes and so on, that are totally beneficial to man. Some of these our science has managed to measure and quantify, but there are many qualities which, as yet, elude our ability to reduce and measure.

Suffice to say, once again, that the true proof is in the eating and that you must do it to benefit from it. Whilst caution is sometimes healthy, our society has become a little too obsessed with wanting "proof" that something works before we try it. Where the activity can at best do no harm and can surely help one's state of mind, then you must be prepared to give the experience a try.

There are certain other possibilities for which you must also be prepared.

You may well discover that your intuitive faculties become more refined and keener. You may even see some colours or halos and auras round the plants and flowers that you study. This is good and perfectly natural. Your awareness is growing and you are simply beginning to attune to those more subtle vibrations and emanations that you were missing before.

This is truly a wonderful step to take, but be prepared to wait a while for this to happen. Also, the perfumes and fragrances around you will appear to change. You will notice more subtlety and greater variety, and even some that you have not experienced ever before. This is wonderful, so give thanks for it.

Possibly your sense of sound will become keener and you may be able to perceive more subtle sounds, and tones. If and when these things occur for you, just enjoy the experience and let the feeling of love grow inside you.

For one patient of mine, I know that this particular area of growth was central to her recovery from serious illness. As her awareness grew, so did her ability to promote physical change in her own body.

It is highly likely too, that you could find changes in your physical body. They may well be so small as to be imperceptible at first, but gradually, slowly yet surely, they will begin to occur. As they do, give thanks for them and thank the elements of nature for their part in your increased sense of well-being, for your rapport with creation is the cornerstone to the balance and harmony that promotes good health.

Do, also be aware, that you may notice changes in palate. They too will be almost unnoticed in the early stages, but they will occur, very gently, so that you will require more of some things and less of others. You must not try to force this, but allow it to come to pass naturally. Just be prepared for it, but do not anticipate it. The maximum is "gradually and gently" with all things.

The truly wonderful feature of this growth will be your increasing love for your world, your immediate environment, your garden, your home, your town, your country, and your global home, other continents and the whole planet.

It is inevitable that you will be evermore sensitive to the maltreatment of your world. You will not only detest the small, obvious abuses, but your sensitivity will not allow you to condone or accept the more insidious and devastating neglects and abuses man is inclined to perpetate, as he separates himself from the planet on which he lives.

You are enjoying a love-affair that will be the greatest in your life. Nothing will compare with it, and it will begin to spill over into all departments of your life, radiating outwards, touching everyone and every circumstance you encounter. By being more loving to your world you will be more loving to yourself and others.

If you have been a hay fever sufferer (and not a sufferer from the chemical sprays abounding in our environment) then this building of closer rapport could help to reduce the symptoms enormously. You will have no aversion to nature and what it can give to you. In fact, you will be coming in closer harmony so that the rejections of any natural phenomena can be assuaged and eliminated.

I must emphasize the word NATURAL here. Not only has our world been ravaged by the often indiscriminate use of chemicals but the pursuit of profit at all cost has led to ecological imbalance, particularly in farming, and we are beset with crops that are not rotated in any way, or with strains and types that are not indigenous to our countryside. Consequently, a sudden introduction of a new type of crop on a wide scale can produce a sometimes staggering imbalance, with all its attendant problems. The massive and sudden increase in the oilseed rape cultivation in East Anglia has proved an immense challenge to those of us sensitive to pollens.

However, we can only hold ourselves responsible and therefore it is only we, who can produce change, and it is through these methods that we can best achieve happy, loving progress, rather than hold protest meetings and write angry letters. By all means be vigilant, but do not lose sight of your true creative power to influence others in more loving, subtle ways, enabling beneficial and positive change.

You know you can do it.

PART 3

LOVING AND BLESSING YOUR WORLD

Here is a statement for you to use that will enable a growing rapport with your world as you grow in love with it. Use it frequently, every day if you can, but certainly once every few days, reading it out at least three times and then thinking and considering it for a few moments.

"I am more and more attuned to the loving power of creation in my world. I give thanks for it and bless it, as it sends its healing and harmonising love to me."

This is a very powerful statement. Use it as often as you can. You will find all the statements I have written throughout this book are repeated at the back, so you can copy them down easily into a pocket book, or better still, on to small cards, enabling you to carry them around with you. Use them often and, of course, adapt them to help you if you wish.

Always do what "feels" right for you, and you must "feel" right when reading a statement. If you don't, then alter it a little until you do.

At an early opportunity, you must begin giving out to your world, as well as drawing in. You are part of the rhythmic breath of life, and therefore you must reflect this in your thought, words, and deeds, so that there is a continuous flowing movement. The power of creation works through all things manifested in it, and that means you and I. We have to become increasingly effective channels for this flow of activity, thoughts and ideas.

One of the greatest facts for us to realize is that which we give away, we keep. I refer once again to the little song in the introduction to this work, which refers to just that principle. Those who have custody over animals, either in some form of husbandry, or in caring for domestic pets, will recognise clearly how this principle works in relation to our animal friends. A neurotic dog owner will send out vibrations and ideas that are reflected in the behaviour of their pet. Many will recognise such a situation from their experience I am sure.

It is equally true that the love given to a pet dog or cat will also be reflected by the object of its attention. This love will be returned many times over, without being sought or requested in any way.

It is equally true, of course, with our fellow man. That which is sent out is that which we receive. Remembering, therefore, that we are all part of the creative Power, it is equally true of our environment in that it truly shares the same source of being. With this in mind, you can bring into your life all the good you seek, drawing upon the delicate, immense, and yet silent power of your world.

Take yourself quietly into your garden, preferably when you are alone or when you will not be disturbed. Alternatively, if you have no garden, go into your backyard, or to your window, and open it wide. Choose a view or outlook that you are accustomed to and that you see (although perhaps ignore) every day.

Look carefully at what you see and make some mental notes of what you can observe. If it is your garden, focus, as you did before, upon the plants and flowers, any trees and shrubs and lawn, except this time look in less detail at what you can see, but rather take in the whole and complete vista before you.

If you find your look across a largely urban landscape from your home, none the less, look around the whole view before you, taking in as much as possible, without dwelling upon detail for very long. Take just a few moments to do this. You may have become very accustomed to this view or locations, taking it for granted, perhaps being somewhat tired of it or hostile to it.

. Whatever the circumstances, ensure that you do the following:

   1. Choose a view that for you represents the true outlook

from where you live — the image you would see in your imagination if asked what you see from your house or home.

2. If at all possible, view it from outdoors, or if this is impossible, from an opened door or window.
3. Scan the width of your vision slowly for a few moments looking at as much as you can of the picture before you.
4. Suspend any judgement of what you see. Try not to either like or dislike at this point but simply see. To help to accomplish this, which many may find difficult, simply pretend you are going to sit down in a few moments and that you will have to describe what you see, in writing, without "looking" at your chosen view again. This may take some practice but it will truly be worth the effort.

Now, when you have finished your scan as I have outlined, read the following statement to yourself, loud and clear, three times. It doesn't matter if you feel silly or embarrassed. Remember, you are changing yourself in the most profound way and all these things add to the depth of change you experience. Just do it and enjoy the benefits. Read:

"I bless my world. I send out my love to my environment in waves of never ending power. I give thanks for the love and care I receive from all I can see. Every part of my world surrounds me with loving care. No harm will ever come to me from the things I live amongst. They offer me their never ending love in power and glory of all creation. I accept it and give my love to them. I love and bless my world. I act and think in loving ways. I am considerate and thoughtful in my deeds and actions. I see my world as a part of me, I love and bless my world, and all that surrounds me."

Choose a day upon which you can concentrate the use of this exercise and this statement. Use the statement on at least one occasion every hour upon the chosen day. Carry it around with you written upon a card or small piece of paper and whenever you have the opportunity, read and use it.

Should you work away from home much of the time, do this from your office or workroom and when you do not feel free to speak out loud, think the statement through silently in the quiet of your mind. If you drive to work along a regular route, (or travel by train or bus) extend the use of this idea to your journey, frequently invoking the statement, if only in your thought.

Always, however, start to use it from your domicile or home, and gradually extend its use to where you travel and work, or study, or perhaps go shopping. See your world like the web of a spider with you in its centre. As you move along its strands, you bless and strengthen them, making them more secure for you to live upon. You are giving a maintenance of the most wonderful and dramatic kind. The positive love, and good thoughts and words you distribute, will be as seed planted along your pathway. As you water and tend them with more of your love, they will germinate, sprout and flower into the most beautiful flowers, and as they do so, just watch your world change for the better.

If you already loved your environment and told it so, that's fine. The good you receive from it and the love you have for it will grow even more. Should you not have been very happy with your home and locations for your daily life, you will notice that they will begin to change, slowly but surely, and a keener sense of belonging and satisfaction will begin its entry into your consciousness. The most important feature of this comes home to roost in the area of your mental and physical health.

As you identify spiritually with your world by blessing and loving it, so you will align yourself with all the possibilities that exist for your god within creation. The rapport that evolves will dissipate adverse stress and debilitating anxieties. No longer will you feel threatened, limited, trapped or bored, but you will be liberated and grow into an understanding of all things for your good being not only

possible, but the correct and normal state of affairs. You will
be free in the flow of the loving power of creation. All things
become possible here. Life will reject the limits you have
mistakenly associated with it, and good health of mind and
body will be central to the ways in which you think and feel.
You will identify with nothing less than that, and the
vibrations of your body will have no choice (or wish) than to
follow the call of your soul and your innermost self.

Love begets love. You are becoming love. That means you
are becoming health.

One patient who used this technique, became increasingly
aware of his love for the simple, even apparently mundane
things in life. Those things which had become a chore, he
now saw in a new light and they were now amongst the most
rewarding activities of his day.

You must understand another very important matter with
all that is set out in this guided journey of becoming a more
loving person. We are creatures of habit and our lives reflect
that all too well at times. What we are doing is changing our
habits from unpleasant ones to positive ones, from fear and
resentment, into love, and from dis-ease into health. However,
we have spent some time (in my case 40 years!) concentrating
on the negative ones, repeatedly pouring them into our
subconscious minds until they have become rather engrained
there. Now we are changing the contents, but the same
principle applies and to truly fill our minds until our
consciousnesses are imbued with these ideas, we have to
repeat and repeat the words and ideas, many many times
over to begin with.

The effect is cumulative. Eventually there will be no room
left for the old ideas as they are ushered out to make way for
the new ones. But you must persist. You must continue to
repeat what you wish to be until it becomes your reality.

It was said "As a man thinketh in his hert (subconscious
mind), so is he." Your mind and body will manifest what
you think of it, and what you say to it, and so will your
world, so stick to it, for the rewards are beyond your boldest
imaginings.

PART 4

LOVING THE EVERYDAY THINGS

It is easy to understand how we think we may love the great moments in our lives, those peak events we experience which it is our right and our place to enjoy. Of course we love those occasions. But all too often we come down rather quickly and painfully too, as soon as the thrill and excitement is over, the event and its glory has left us, and we find we are back in the day to day living which, by comparison, will seem drab and uninteresting, and certainly not deserving of such power of emotion and love. Yet it is through the "so-called" mundane that we truly live and grow. It is those day to day activities that afford us our greatest opportunities for growth and achievement, and many a philosopher and mystic would agree that it is often the little things we do which help to shape us and mould our character, offering the possibility of true spiritual growth.

It is our view of anything that determines the effect it has upon us, and whilst not suggesting an abundance of rose-tinted spectacles will change our world, I know that our reaction and attitude is paramount.

When we see life as a series of small unimportant nuisances to be hastily "got out of the way" with as little inconvenience as possible; when it is only the "highs", the exciting, one-off highlights that seem to make our lives worth living, then we are truly not living at all.

Someone close to me recently graduated from University having obtained an extremely good honours degree. He did this against great odds, where others might have "thrown in the towel" and simply given up.

We were all delighted for him, and showed the joy that such effort deservedly brings to the recipient and those who have helped and encouraged him.

After graduation however, the reality he faces is either a

period of unemployment, or possibly working in a job for which he is considerably over-qualified.

He can view this in two ways. He can either resent the situation in which he, like many graduates, finds himself, or he can take life as it comes, realising that opportunity is ever present, and that, with patience, he can enjoy the boring mundane work until something more suitable is found. He may also find that his talents will be channelled in ways he could never consider possible. If he is prepared to view life as a loving experience, one in which he can grow, then the perfect situation will present itself to him. It is up to him.

In the meantime, he must love life for its own sake, even the trivial, day to day affairs, looking forward to more and more "great" days to come.

Those of us who have been privileged to be parents, will know the truth of this idea. It is often the small, apparently inconsequential occurrences, that hold the greatest positive affection in one's consciousness. The birthday card given by a loving young daughter which is simply a mass of coloured squiggles and marks, nonetheless, in years to come, will remind the recipient of that treasured moment when love flowed free in his affairs, in a simple, direct way.

My young son has given me his first piece of "woodwork" from nursery school. It consists of a block of wood with two nails hammered into it at unusual angles, and another strip of wood screwed on for luck. I know in years to come that the memory stirred by this artefact so lovingly given, will help to lift the spirit, should the need occur.

Oftentimes, when people have passed into the next life, and our grief and sorrow have subsided, it is the everyday things that we recall. Their smile, their mannerisms and favourite expressions, the way they combed their hair or fastened their coat, and even perhaps their frown or little idiosyncrasies, these are the very qualities that remind us vividly of them, and even those things that once we saw as the reason for irritation and impatience on our part, are transformed to become 'fond memories that we love and cherish so dearly.

How one can long for the 'phone call from the parent who still scolded us in middle-age as if we were a child. How the memory of the exhausting boisterousness of our young children is cherished when they are in adulthood, perhaps pursuing life many, many miles away from us.

It is important for us always to both see, and understand, the significance of everything that happens to us in our lives in the context of opportunity. This is not easy, but of course nothing worth achieving ever is, and I know that the greatest strides I have made in my own life are those that have required the most effort on my part.

Everything surely is an opportunity. Life is about opportunity, and we have to love life and the possibilities it places into our pathway. It is like the view along a motorway compared to that of a country lane. One is the result of the need or demand for haste through life, the other more the consequence of a natural, leisurely development of travel. I know which route offers the most attractive and lovable setting for my eyes to gaze upon, albeit at a slower speed.

We have to re-educate ourselves into the understanding that life is not about haste, getting things done and "out of the way", for it is in living in this fashion that we have sown the seeds of anxiety, fear, depression and guilt. Our minds seldom settle on one project or idea before they are bombarded (if we allow it) by an attack of "must be done by's" or "we can't manage that" or "I can't cope with its" or "I should have done so and so".

We are meant to live in a considered fashion, with each step and action we take being calm, purposeful and complete. Even a top athlete, running the race of his life, can only compete effectively if he is relaxed beforehand, and if he is not to suffer permanent injury, the only tension his body should experience should be that indicated by the fleeting requirement of the moment, for prolonged tension will cause severe harm both to the athlete's muscles and to your life.

In order that you may understand how you can re-discover the love of those small events in your life, there are a few things I shall give you to do. Follow them through, thoroughly. You must understand that it is essential for you to do what I say with as much conviction as possible, so that you will reap the full benefit of these ideas.

I ask you to isolate some of the most tedious and boring chores that you have to do in your day to day work. It may be that you are a housewife who is for ever washing soiled clothing, or hasting through the supermarket before meeting the children from school.

Perhaps you have to spend much of your day answering routine queries on the telephone, or laboriously filing invoices into cabinets. Whatever you select, just write it down on a piece of paper in large capital letters.

1 Sit back and look at it carefully and remember the last occasion that you performed this particular task.
2 Now consider what would happen if you didn't do it. Think of this very carefully. Imagine that this task, from now on, is not going to be done by you or by anyone else. It is going to be left, come what may, because it is boring and tedious, something you certainly don't love doing.
3 Think of all the people who would suffer if this chosen task is not done — family, friends, clients, employers, husband or wife and so on. If it is part of your work in a social service, think of all the needy people who would be either inconvenienced or upset. Imagine the financial losses your business or employer may suffer. See your husband or children wearing dirty clothing, or your wife trying to buy food without any money.
4 Imagine next, how YOU will suffer if people withdraw their attention and labour from the boring, tedious chores and jobs they have to do. The supermarket shelves would be empty, the car would have no petrol, the water wouldn't flow when you turned the tap on, the mail wouldn't come, your clothes wouldn't be pressed and so on and so on!

   The list is endless! Life would come to a standstill. Just think about it. If nobody washed the dishes or swept the road.

5 Think of every small thing that you do, for other people, however irksome it has appeared to you at times. Write each one down and as you do so I ask you to read the following statement to yourself three times, loud and clear: "Every task that I undertake, I do so to help my fellow man. Everything I do is to help life go along in a smooth and happy way. Everything I do is important and I choose to do it with love, to the best of my ability.

Whenever I do something in haste, or in a hurry, just to get through it, I devalue the present moment, and so I devalue myself.

I now see that all things, however small, are important for me and for others, so I do all things with love and care."

6 Carry this statement around with you, and read it and say it often. The evening following your reading of this page, spend a few moments concentrating and then reflecting upon this statement, until you understand it and know it well. In a sense, it is the most important one in this book for when you can get your attitudes right at this point, and you can truly learn to love the small things in life that you do for others, then everything else will slot into place. Love the small things and the big things will take care of themselves.

Read this statement at least every day, for 7 days, and then once or twice a week.

Spend time each and every day, considering how you are able to improve the quality of other people's lives by what you do for them in little, apparently inconsequential ways, and how you can improve what you do, by doing it lovingly.

I remember once, someone said to me that she felt "little more than a slave". She was referring to the fact that her family showed little appreciation for what she did for them. But the important point to understand here is that she usually did what she did for them, grudgingly. There was little or no love in the meals she prepared, or in the lunches she packed, and when you don't put love in, there is none to come out.

The secret is that when we put love into everything we do for others, then they too will respond in a like manner. They will feel and perceive the difference even if they don't meet you, for your loving attitude will show through in ways you cannot even imagine.

A greengrocer I once knew would spend much time arranging a display of fresh fruit in his window and he would enjoy every moment of it. His shop was always full of customers, despite competition from larger and sometimes cheaper stores, for this act of love conveyed so much to those who saw it.

By using the technique and statement I have described you begin to transform your experiences. They take on a new complexion, and you will begin to enjoy doing those things that once bored and irritated you.

You will notice that this will also be reflected in what is done for you by others. There is a dynamic of life in operation which will lead to you drawing into your life, that which you give out. It is reaping and sowing — just wait and see!

You will probably see a change in your long term attitudes and a gradual change in values. In the words of the son, you will discover that "little things mean a lot".

PART 5

LOVING AND BLESSING YOUR LIFE

As a child, I was encouraged to say Grace before meals. This
is a very valuable practice for many, many reasons.

At one level, the saying of Grace helps the meal to become
precisely what it should always be, a "coming together" of
the family or group, to pause from activity, and to refuel and
recharge their systems. It is important that meals should be
consumed in a relatively calm and tranquil atmosphere, with
all irritations and distractions being removed or eliminated as
far as is at all possible.

Sadly our current social climate tends to discourage this.
We have "working lunches", an appalling idea, since, so
often, stressful boardroom conflict is reserved for this time.
And if you stop to think of the physical focus for much
emotional trauma, you will see at once the folly in such a
practice. Our stomachs digest more than our food!

Many schools, hospitals and public institutions cater only
for speedy eating, and we live in a "fast food" age. It is hardly
surprising that we now see such a vast amount of digestive
disease in Western Society. Our "fast food" habits have
resulted in the production of foodstuffs which are often
nutritionally bankrupt and, in some cases, quite harmful if
eaten regularly.

Meal times are important, so I offer here some guidelines
to assist in the development of a practice that will not make
meals something else to be "got through", but rather
occasions of enjoyment and replenishment.

1 Allow at least thirty minutes for each meal.
2 Talk as little as possible, and pursue only that conversation
  which is gentle and light. Within a family group this is
  perfectly feasible.
3 Ensure the environment encourages a relaxed state.
  Telephone off the hook — T.V. and radio off, or only

gentle, happy music with positive associations. No "News" bulletin or newspaper should be allowed near the table and letters should be opened elsewhere.

4 Share something each meal. If it is impossible to serve from separate dishes at the table, share some water or bread with each other.

5 All start together, after the saying of Grace, either out loud or privately.

Point five is the really important one. Not only will the loving and blessing of the food be the perfect way to centre all attention on the meal, but also another dynamic effects you here.

In Kirlian photographic experiments, it has been noticed that the halo or aura around food that has been prepared, actually expands once the food has been loved and blessed. It is part of the Law of Life. The aura shows the vitality of the food, as it does of all things and this increased glow means the food is responding to your thoughts and feeling. It is the real principle of living. Send love and you get it back, seven-fold!

Before each meal, or indeed any occasion that you are about to eat, be still for a few moments, close down thoughts of all around you, and say the following:

"I love and bless that which is given to me to eat and drink. It is imbued with the loving power that created me and all things, and I give thanks for that which is given to me. I thank those who have enabled these good things to come to me, and I send them thoughts of love. I love and bless these fruits of goodness, and the life with which they bless me".

During this time picture in your mind, those who grow and prepare your food and love them for so helping you.

If you can say those words out loud, do so, and if it is possible, say them together, as a group, or in turns, a meal at a time.

I can assure you that by adopting the above attitudes and

practices, not only will mealtimes become much more enjoyable occasions, but they will also be more beneficial for you. Good foods that you once disliked, you will grow to love, and that which is not necessary, or perhaps unsuitable, will gradually disappear from your diet.

Your palate will inevitably change, a little at least, and you will find an unwillingness to nibble and eat between meals if this has been a problem or negative habit. For you are (re-) learning to give respect to the food you eat, for it is the fuel for your body, the temple of your mind and spirit, and you will feel less and less inclined to indulge in bad habits, such as walking around while eating so-called snacks. You are growing and renewing, and as you grow and flower so beautifully, your respect for all things is increased. "How could I have ever treated the fruits of the earth, or my stomach, with such inconsiderate, bad manners", you will say to yourself!

A word here, for the devoted preparers of meals, from the chefs in an expensive restaurant, to the mum who is queen of her kitchen, seeing to the needs of others every day, and not forgetting those who live alone, catering for themselves most of the time.

Do remember that preparing food is an act of love. The feelings and attitudes that are felt during the making of a meal are certain to be transmitted to those who subsequently eat it. Be aware that you are so important in the process of helping another to sustain his life and health, and that you give each and every piece of food, each and every drink, a unique and special quality. It becomes a gift from you to those for whom it is intended, and it should be respected as such.

You may also find that, because of an increased respect for the food you eat, that you will begin to eat only that volume of food which you need. You can leave behind the days of overeating, of diets and calorie counting. Endorse this statement and use it frequently.

"I eat only that which I need. I eat only that which is good for me. I love to be my healthy, ideal weight, at all times. I eat only that which I need. A loving me, is a healthy me. A healthy me is a perfect me, at my ideal body weight".

Read the statement often and enjoy it. When you first use it, speak the words three times, and then close your eyes. Think through the words once more and allow the images to flow in your mind's eye, enjoying simple healthy food, as you remain trim and fit, the ideal body weight for you.

See the image as clearly as you can. Notice how healthy you are, how active you are, how the sunlight shines upon your healthier, stronger body. Hold on to this image for a while and then say, "thank you", for what you see and endorse the new you by saying in the quiet of your mind, "I love my healthy body and the healthy diet I have".

If you have a weight problem use this statement often. However, the idea will be given greater power if taken as part of "Loving Yourself", later in this book. For the meantime, concentrate upon loving the fit, correct image of yourself as you consume the food prepared and given to you with love, whatever your present state of health.

I know some may say that their particular food is often prepared grudgingly or in a bad-tempered way. This may be so, at least in appearance, but it is imperative that you realise that, first and foremost, this is only a temporary action, and also you must understand that even a meal thus prepared, will have in it the love of those who grew or manufactured the food. And if the irascible parent or mate truly did not have some love in their heart, they would not prepare anything for you at all.

Even more important, you are taking responsibility for creating a more loving world around you. You are taking the initiative and through the change in your attitudes, they will change also. You will be surprised at how this happens as you live more lovingly.

CREEPY CRAWLIES

As a very young child, I grew up in a poor quarter of bomb-shattered North London. In that post-war urban environment, there wasn't really much opportunity for contact with nature although we had a little garden which we shared with the other tenants in our house.

I loved the spring and summer. I could go out into the garden, whenever I wished, on those warmer, sunnier days, and enjoy playing on the grass, looking at the flowers, and inhaling the scent from the lilac tree. Away from the half-destroyed houses, the bomb-craters, and the economic hardship, this was indeed a secure little paradise for me.

I can recall many happy episodes there, but one in particular, comes to mind. I was chasing a cat in our garden when I stubbed my toe on a stone. I stopped and turned the stone over to reveal a host of small creatures, wriggling and scampering. There were all sorts of little bugs, creepy crawlies as you might call them, yet I can clearly remember being transfixed by this sight. They certainly didn't frighten or revolt me at all for, at that young age, little or no prejudice had dampened my consciousness. I seemed to appreciate that these creatures were as much part of God's plan as I was, and I had intruded in their little world for a while. There was a real sense of wonder for what I beheld, and it has never left me.

The picture is as vivid today as ever it was, and I am happy to be one of those souls loathe to harm a fly unnecessarily, even today.

Now, there were two possible reactions to what I saw. I could have adopted the standard practice of biased adulthood, and expressed horror and revulsion at such unlovely, slimy things, that had the effrontery to pollute my garden. But, I didn't.

I was wide-eyed and surprised at the diversity of God's creation, of the life that manifests in so many different animated patterns, underneath an ordinary stone in my little garden. In their place, their right to life was as my own, and the sheer complexity of design and structure they demonstrated was quite breathtaking.

My attitude was the same as that of many young children,

still uncluttered by negative thinking. When seen through the eyes of a child, these little creatures were to be loved and respected as part of all life. They were yet another indication of the superb and masterful variety of possibilities within all creation.

Our reaction to all things determines the quality of our lives. We must not let preconceived ideas and bad influences, dictate to us how we are going to feel about anything, any situation, or indeed anybody. It is up to us to ensure we go forward in life, loving the experience of simply "being", and realising that we have, in the palms of our hands, the power to see any situation in a positive, calm way, and transmute even the most apparently difficult circumstances into opportunities.

We must change our vocabulary. Difficulties become challenges or opportunities. Fears dissolve into excitement and wonder. Illness or disease can become renewal. And creepy-crawlies become God's creatures too.

As we lift up the stones on the pathway of life, inevitably we shall see many things that puzzle us and, that we may perhaps have become accustomed to fearing and resisting. But our life is about our growth, morally, physically, and emotionally, spiritually and mentally. That which we run away from will always reappear for our scrutiny, and it is up to us to control our lives. The way we respond determines what a situation will become. If we see ourselves as dominant, working with the positive, loving power of creation flowing through us, then we become invincible agents for good, both in our lives, and in the lives of others.

There are three rules here for you to put into operation:

i First, you must recognise and bless every situation you meet in your life. Before you make any judgement, you must remember that you are a loving being, a part of the loving flow of life, with all the immense, creative power that brings to you. Whatever you face, know that you can, by sending only love, transform it into your good. You have the power, in the moment, to do just that. I have proved this so to my satisfaction many, many times and, for example, I have seen a cancer scare become temporary anaemia, easily healed.

ii Secondly, you must live in the knowledge that there is no challenge that you will meet, for which you are not completely equipped, in body, mind and spirit. Whatever you face, you can overcome it, in a completely satisfactory way. As part of this idea it is very important to realise that what you encounter in life, is right for you. It is not right, necessarily, for somebody else so don't try to pass the buck or rely too much on others. The situation is there for you and you can only benefit from negotiating it in a calm, positive, loving way. It is a chance to grow.

iii As a third thought, remember that it is your attitudes that determine those things and those people that come into your life. You are becoming a Child of unconditional, free flowing love, and as you see the loving, good possibilities in all things and all people, accordingly you will attract those elements to you. "Birds of a feather, flock together", is a true law of life, applicable both to people and to circumstances. If you are meeting too many situations that you find negative and worrying, then spend a little more time using the earlier parts of this book. The prize is great and worth every effort you can give.

Next time you "turn over a stone" in your life, be sure to understand that those things revealed to you are for your good, and will help to mould a wiser, stronger, more loving you.

Take a few moments in the stillness at this point. Close your eyes and relax for a few moments, withdrawing from the sensory world around you. Think of your breath, the gentle movement of life that flows in and out of your being, giving to you all the goodness you need to be healthy and alive, full of vitality. Feel the breath flow in and out, for a few moments. Then recall that this most important element for your being is freely given to you, and is available in a limitless supply.

Think on that.

Your life is just the same. All that you truly need is readily available now. You have to recognise this fact. Even at a material level, this is so. All that you need is always available for you. True, your own consciousness may limit its manifestation because of fear-based, limited thinking, but none-the-less, it all exists for you.

If you won the Football Pools tomorrow, and obtained a First Dividend of enormous size, the money with which you will have to be paid, exists already. It wouldn't be printed specially. The money is already in circulation and a circumstance would attract it into your life, and make you rich over night. Everything that made this possible existed *before* you won the money. It was a bringing together of situations and actions that allowed a chain of events to occur around you.

You can be a millionaire in every sense in your life. Set off as many chain reactions as you can, and then feel them affect you. You must ensure that these chain reactions are for your good (and the good of others) sparked off in a positive manner, wrapped in loving thoughts and sentiments.

Of course, we can't all win the football pools, and for most of us it wouldn't be in our best interest, however we might feel that it would. But both health and happiness, and indeed wealth, are truly states of mind, and we can, through our thoughts and actions, bring to pass health and prosperity, love and happiness, in each and every department of our lives. It simply depends upon our attitudes and how they precipitate action in our affairs. Good thoughts and actions reap the similar harvest. Couch these in love, and the world is yours for sure! You get to keep only that which you give away!

Here is a powerful statement for you to read and learn. It will convert and transform, so write it upon a card or piece of paper, and carry around with you for a day, reading often, and out aloud whenever possible:

"I recognise each event in my life as an opportunity. I understand that Universal Love flows through me, touching all things and all people I meet along my path. People, animals, events and circumstances, I touch them all with love, and I make my way a happy and enriching one. . .

There is nothing I meet in my day that I cannot manage. All things become possible as I flow with love, and I meet my good in all situations and people, feeling safe, secure and confident".

When you have read this three times, reflect quietly upon it, and allow the words to glide and float through your mind. Never be embarrassed by being loving. You are not becoming "gushing" or "sloppy"; you are simply becoming quietly powerful and in control, so go on, flood them all with your love.

PART 6

LITTLE TIN SOLDIERS

As a little boy, I loved my tin soldiers, especially those in bright coloured tunics and uniforms. They carried my mind far away to interesting places and lands I had never visited, and we had many exciting journeys together. I frequently had to repair them, fixing on broken heads with matchsticks, so that the wounded ones could continue in the fray. The broken soldiers were as important to me as those that had remained intact; I loved them all.

Often, as we get older, we reject those things, that have been of good service to us. They tend to be regarded as obsolete, rather prematurely, part of our past and we are encouraged by our "throw-away" orientated society to think and act in this way.

I am not suggesting that we become over sensitive to the possessions we have, for in trying to hold or not let go, we create problems of attachment, which are difficult for us to overcome. All we have is given to us in a stewardship capacity, to care for and value for its contribution to our lives and our expeiences upon our path of growth. But it is important for us to really understand the true value of that which we are given.

The old bone-shaker of a car which supported many family holidays, is often more cherished than the sleek new machine we may acquire in more affluent later life. It is not so much a sentimental attachment to the metal and fabric that we develop, but rather a deep stirring within us for the memories its image provokes, for the ups and downs we shared and the love that helped us overcome them.

We forever seek the new, and, in certain respects that is fine. It is part of the reason for our being that we have a very slight dissatisfied edge to our accomplishments, for he that feels totally satisfied, is in danger of procrastinating, and that opposes the laws of life.

But equally damaging is the reckless and uncaring pursuit of the new and different, so that all we have ever had is hardly recognised for its true worth.

We tend only to cherish things when we no longer have them. We miss friends and relatives when they have died, or have moved far away from us. We only appreciate health when we are sick. Wealth is best appreciated by those who are poor. When things are removed from our experience, it is then that we become aware of their true value to us and we then understand how we have neglected our loving understanding and appreciation of them.

The man confined to a wheel chair knows the value of walking.

Does this mean therefore, that we must love all things? Simply, yes. We must treasure each tiny part of our experience as we go through life. If Man really loved his world, neither would he make weapons of destruction, nor would he pollute the fields and rivers that are his home. It is Man's lack of true perception and understanding, a consequence of unloving indifference, that allows these negative and damaging creations to manifest. It is necessary for us all to dedicate ourselves to the loving creative flow of life. It is imperative and urgent that we link with it and become imbued with its essence, for only then will our lives begin to work out happily and successfully. It is by living within this flow that we can make disease, sorrow, pain, poverty and so on, facets of a past consciousness where we allowed ourselves to be disenfranchised victims of the "slings and arrows of outrageous fortune".

Instead of feeling the effects, we have to become in tune with the creative cause of life and that cause is love.

It is the love that says thank you, with kind words and thoughts.

It is the love that carries a burden for another, without expecting reward.

It is the love that wishes for another, first, that good it has sought for itself.

It is the love that never has to be asked.

It is the love that makes whole, calms and restores, where all seemed lost.

It is the love which makes no demand.

It is the love that shares all it has with you each and every day.

Frequently, in films and books, we hear a tear-besmirched heroine, plaintively ask her beau, to "make love to her". I have always found this a ridiculous and most inappropriate expression, for what is after all, a usually selfish and negative request. The true loving between partners, of course may find a beautiful flowing in physical harmony and mental union, but to refer to physical gratification as love is really a complete misunderstanding of the idea. Love is often willingness to release and let go.

For a parent, the marriage of a son or daughter is usually a true test of such love, for the parent's ability to allow that which is best for the offspring, is surely tried and tested. We have to learn and understand that absolutely nothing belongs to us, and it is how we cope with such a truth, that determines how loving we really are. After all, we come into this world with nothing, and we certainly leave it without our material acquisitions. The love we share with our world and others is what we keep, nothing else. So start getting a good bank balance of that precious currency now.

On a day-to-day basis, we should bless and encase in love all our activities.

The car journey taken for granted, should be dedicated for the good of all, both yourself and other drivers. I frequently use the following statement prior to a journey.

"My journey is God's journey. I drive secure in the love of infinite wisdom. I do no harm to others, and others do no harm to me as we are all protected, journeying upon God's loving road."

You will find the use of such a statement will change the nature of your travel. You experience fewer hold-ups, and generally your travel will be smoother and happier. If you are to travel with another driver, you can use the following:

"I am safe and happy as I journey with my friend. He is guided by the flow of creative wisdom and love, and takes me perfectly to my destination".

Let the act of dedicating and blessing your activities become a feature of your life, and then, just watch the quality of your life improve.

Before decorating your house, dedicate your work to the perfect pattern of life, and see the creative genius of love in each task you undertake, even the washing of your paint brushes! In such a way you can transform your experiences from the mundane to the worthwhile and interesting, from the frightening to the enjoyable. Life will become a more beautiful experience, saturated with meaningful episodes and opportunities that you can sail through for you will be supported by the greatest power and energy in the universe — the power of love.

The preparation of a meal is an act of love and when involved in such an activity, it is important to realise that your mood and thought patterns will influence the final offering you have for those for whom it is intended. Not only will the final product look and taste better when prepared with a loving heart, but it will also make those who partake of it feel so much better, for your love will be transmitted and carried by each morsel of food eaten.

Never again prepare a meal in a state of anxiety or anger. Make loving thoughts and blessings become your appetizers. Keep the following statement written upon a card in your kitchen, so that you can see it at all times when cooking and preparing food. Allow it to be your "mood-settler" before you even slice some bread for toasting.

"This food I prepare, I bless with love to enrich those who partake of it. I offer all food and drink as a gift, to bless the lives of others as we share the wonderful bounty of creation".

As you read and say this statement, in your mind's eye, see your family, friends (or even customers, should you run a restaurant) enjoying the wonderful food you have given to them. Feel the warmth and satisfaction grow within you as you realize what an important role you have in helping others by preparing food for them. However much people like the food you prepare already, I guarantee they will find it even more nutritious and enjoyable when you adopt this approach to your time in the kitchen, just wait and see.

There is no task or activity too ordinary or too small for this kind of attention. It is important that you start with the small and apparently insignificant things for, in this way, you are building from a firm foundation so that you will not be inclined to slip back into negative and unloving ways. Being loving will have become a habit for you.

Before you post your next batch of letters, briefly hold each one, sending a thought of love and blessing to the recipient. In this way, you will transmit to others a feeling of well-being and happiness which they will always associate with communication with you. This will have enormous benefits, enhancing whatever the contents of the letter may be. From a business point of view this will have obvious advantages and will help to promote smoother, happy business relationships, even when there are apparent difficulties to be dealt with.

Should you have ever been the unfortunate recipient of a hostile letter, you will be aware of that extra, negative energy, far greater than the ink upon the page, that can so upset if you allow it so to do.

Of course, such a destructive letter, ultimately as a "come-back" effect upon its sender, for such are the laws that govern our lives, but it does illustrate how a more positive approach will create a healthy state of affairs in your dealings with others, both the written and "viva voce".

If you are about to make a telephone call that you have been dreading for some reason or another, use the following statement, three times, before dialling the number:

"I make this call with a powerful, loving heart, expecting and knowing I shall experience the perfect response".

However difficult you may find such an idea, none-the-less, do it, and do it each time you have to make a call that you have found difficult to approach. You will find that, as you use the ideas in this book, such occurrences will be less and less likely but in the early days, you may find it useful.

Persistence is the key with all the ideas I offer to you. Even when faced with what appears to be apparent failure, keep on, for sometimes, within the laws of healing, things can temporarily appear to become worse before they get better. This doesn't mean you have to experience disaster, but it does mean that you have to recognise that as old bad habits and vibrations around you are being washed away, they sometimes have one final attempt to hang on and seek to dig their claws further into your spiritual flesh. Even the best ointment can make the flesh smart a little before healing takes place.

It is also important to realize that, whatever you do in life to improve and grow, you will soon begin to forget just how bad things have been blessed with a capacity to forget, but sometimes it can blurr the edges of our vision a little too much and so we have to remember we are building, brick upon brick, and even if we never see the foundation stones again, without them, the temple gate of our life could not stand securely and firmly.

I had a back problem that had gradually been healed. Suddenly, after a period of a few years, a long spell of travelling and fixed sitting, brought the problem on again very severely. I had forgotten just how painful and incapacitating the conditon had been. I had forgotten just how beautifully and gently I had been healed, only to allow a period of bad habits and enforced poor posture to bring the problem to the surface again.

We all tend in life, to forget just how much progress we have made.

I ask you now to choose a task you have always disliked performing. It may be mowing the lawn, it may be ironing shirts, or perhaps hoovering the stairs. Whatever it is, sit quietly for a few moments and close your eyes. I want you to imagine that you are doing that task now. See yourself doing it as clearly as you can. Remember the odours and perfumes that accompany the task. Recall all the physical sensations that you possibly can, the noises, the aching limbs, the sweat on your brow. Whatever helps you to recall the experience, think of it now.

Now let the experience go, let it leave you.

Open your eyes and read this statement to yourself.

"I have allowed myself to be conditioned so that I dislike *this task*. (substitute with name, e.g. decorating, house-work, etc). I know *this task* helps to make my life, and the lives of others better and more enjoyable. I now choose to tackle *this task* with loving care and thoroughness. It is my joy to do this task in a perfect way, for it is important and worthy of my best attention and I treat it so".

Then close your eyes again, and see yourself standing back, proudly inspecting the excellent paintwork, or pristine stairway or whatever the correct, complete image is for your selection. See it as being done perfectly. If it is something that you have not found easy to do, for lack of experience or knowledge, or whatever, see the job done perfectly and see those for whom it is intended, happy and smiling, grateful for what you have done for them.

Using this technique, you can and will transform even negative experiences into positive ones. Your attitudes to them will change, and so will the task and the experiences. There will be fewer hitches and mishaps, and you will actually begin to enjoy doing things you have loathed. What is most important is that you will do a better job more quickly and more effectively than ever before. And others, too, will express greater appreciation of what you do.

I have always had a dislike of decorating. In part, at least, it stemmed from a lack of faith in my own abilities at a practical level, and also from the fact that my father, too, had always disliked spending time in such activity. Others had often criticised and ridiculed this dear man's attempts and efforts in an area where he had received no instructions or guidance. A wall needing fresh wall paper, or a ceiling crying out for a new coat of paint, was often a focus for domestic conflict!

I was able to begin to change and transform this feeling by dedicating this work I did to my family, my wife and children. The painting of a bedroom for my two boys became enjoyable, creative experience which was reflected in the best job of work I had ever done in decorating. I am not suggesting that I became expert overnight, but by making the work an act of love for those I share my life with, the experience was transformed and I was able to see what I did in its true, unselfish light. I was no longer simply trapped in misery amid nauseating paint fumes. Rather, I was trying to create a better environment for those I loved, and as I changed my attitude, I also grew to love those for whom I worked more and more. I had simply lost sight of the true motive for what I did. Instead of trying to enhance the value of the house, I was making a brighter home for us all.

I suggest that one dislike is taken at a time here. Don't go for an over-load because you will become confused and perhaps perturbed. Just take one thing at a time. Each time that you do so, you will find the next task easier and so, on it will go, until you will look back and wonder, "what on earth was all the fuss about?"

When you have successfully achieved in any situation that you had formerly failed or disliked, congratulate yourself. It is very important that you give yourself a pat on the back for what you have done. You are then ready to apply the same principle to another one of your pet hates or dislikes.

PART 7

KNOWING YOURSELF IS
LOVING YOURSELF

It is something of a shock to us to discover that which we observe in others is a reflection of ourselves.

I recall speaking to a young lady once who had come to me for help. She was very troubled. She was living in a state of fear due to her involvement in a long standing argument over the misappropriation of monies. A rather nasty situation had developed, and she was tormented by the idea of legal threats from a third party, although she was relatively free of blame herself. She had become afraid to go out. She was depressed, even a little suicidal.

Although much time had elapsed and I felt sure no such threat existed, if indeed it had ever done, she still dreaded a court summons arriving at her home.

I asked her why she felt so sure that the other people involved in the affair, would try such a pointless, malicious ploy, designed only to cause her pain and distress?

At first she said that she didn't really know, and could not understand their motives at all. Gradually, however, she began to speak of her own anger and frustration at what had occurred, and her feelings of powerlessness to recover that which she saw as her own. In fact, she felt let down and very bitter about the whole situation.

When I pressed her further, it became obvious that this was the type of action she had considered instigating herself at one time. The feelings of anger and resentment she feared so much in others were actually inside her, and she was merely identifying these same qualities in them. This young lady was viewing parts of herself, mirrored in the threats and behaviour of others.

We tend to attract that which we give away. I encouraged her to work at transmuting the feelings of hate into feelings of compassion and, most important of all, to work at identifying the positive qualities within herself, for she was merely attributing her own negative thoughts to other people. And, of course, in time, they were quite likely to respond, meeting like with like.

The best way to change a situation is to change your view of it. Our perception governs the way our consciousness will work, and it is the workings of our consciousness that determines what happens to us from day to day.

Be rich in thought and you will be rich in life.

Be happy in thought and happiness will be yours.

Be loving in thought and you will be much loved.

And it is love that creates, builds, harmonises and heals.

In order that we may have a healthy mind and body we have to love ourselves. We have to recognise in ourselves those masterful, infinite qualities which make us remarkable, unique individuals of the most incredible potential.

All that we ever need to know or understand is already available to us, easily and freely, for within our consciousness is access to the infinite power of creation which links us to all knowledge and wisdom to answer questions, both great and small.

When we have a challenge to meet or a problem to solve, the true answers are already within us. Our world is ours to use, to love and protect and all that man has ever needed is revealed to him in the right place, at the right time.

If we can learn to understand that, then we truly have the keys to the kingdom.

As we meet a problem our reactions are often conditioned to be frantic in our search for a solution. We may seek the answer in a book or library. We may look for the answer by asking a friend. We usually tend to reach outside and away from ourselves, feeling that it is only elsewhere that real knowledge rests, and that we are not able to cope alone.

Well, first and foremost, we must understand that all our knowledge already exists. There are no inventions, no discoveries, there are only re-discoveries as we re-learn some things long forgotten in the mists of time. In his book "The Awakening Earth" Peter Russell describes the repetitive nature of pattern and form in creation, so that in particle physics we find relationships which resemble those of the planets in our solar system. Our solar system is almost cerainly the "particle physics" of another, greater level of consciousness, at another level of reality. Within the idea of the Wisdom and Infinite Power that created our cosmos, called God, Creator, Infinite Spirit, Big Bang or whatever, rests the inescapable knowledge that we human beings are almost certainly the equivalent to atoms within the cell structure of the body of our Creator, and that we share with that Wise Power, all the potential and knowledge it expresses.

If God or our Creator is wise, then potentially, so are we. If the Infinite Mind that made us is all knowing and all powerful, so then, can we be, for this is the animating part of us which is a spark of that Creator, and it is this which gives us access to all knowledge and all that brings in its wake.

Nothing man has built or made has been inspired by reference points outside of him. Every structure that man has assembled has come from within him, and it has its counterpart, somewhere within his physical and mental being.

In her book "The Fifth Dimension", Vera Stanley Alder illustrates this point beautifully. Each bridge built has its form and mechanical device already available somewhere within the body of man, and the structures of nature. As we construct wonderful, breathtaking machines, it is to the patterns that are extant that we form that which we create. We do not initiate nature, nor it is not that we deliberately copy that which we see around. It is simply that within the natural, Divine Laws, we have no choice. The things we build will only operate within the patterns that already exist. Just as the snowflake forms to the hexagon of infinite variation and possibility, so too, do man's creations and inventions conform to the infinite patterns and ideas of the Cosmos. Otherwise they would be formless and unstable.

Within us is the wisdom and knowledge of all ages.

Within you is the wisdom and knowledge for everything

you will ever need, and everything that you will ever seek to do.

Once there were no books, no libraries. Henry Ford had no workshop manual, apart from that vision within him. There he used the workshop manual of life.

Within you is the power and knowledge to be just as you would wish to be. That makes you a truly remarkable being, with limitless possibility in all that you do.

Of course, we all benefit from the knowledge of those who have gone before us. We benefit for their intuitive thinking, their application and researches. I would not suggest that you never read another book, for that would be very foolish.

But it is important to utilize the same source as all great men — Einstein, Jung and so on. It is essential for you to link your thought with the great creative Power of the Universe and to draw upon the Infinite, boundless knowledge that dwells there, ready, free and waiting.

What has this to do with loving yourself?

Well, for a start, let us look at the possibilities that being a true spark of creation implies.

It means that there is nothing to which you cannot aspire. Anything that you seek to do or be is within your grasp, or you simply would not be able to even "fantasize" upon it.

If you are able to imagine a possibility for yourself, then THAT IS TRULY NOW A POSSIBILITY FOR YOU. If you are able to see yourself achieving something, then it is within your power to achieve it.

Now it would be rather foolish of me to sit and imagine myself playing centre-forward for the England Football team, for, had that been within the plan of my life, it would have already been accomplished, and I would certainly not have left it until middle-age. Also, my lack of belief in that possibility, did not allow it to appear often enough in my mind's eye so that I strove to make it happen!

But just as the healer must see only perfection in his sick patient, and just as the landscape gardener can see beauty and order amongst neglect and rubble, and hold the image steady while he brings it nearer to manifestation, so, too, can you bring to pass in your life, all that you perceive and hold firm too.

Fix beauty in your consciousness and you will attract it to you. Fill your mind with love and love is what you will become.

All that you seek to be resides within you, and all that you have to do is set it free.

That makes you a truly remarkable being. Your potential is unlimited for in you dwells the power that both made you and makes all things.

The hustle bustle of life tends to dent our halos. Stress and disease occurs usually when our self-image is battered, and when we have begun to struggle to make things work.

A few years ago my halo had been fed through a shredder and ripped into tiny pieces. But I now realise that it was only my halo, and once the damage was repaired, my potential remained the same to be the happy, healthy, successful person I once was. Very gradually, I learned all over again how to love myself and to respect my abilities.

You can do exactly the same. No matter from what point you commence, you can start now, to turn your image of yourself into a positive, powerful loving one.

How?

Let's start feeding in some good ideas and good memories. However dull and uninteresting you may think you are. However sick, or ill you may think you feel. However useless and hopeless things appear, don't give in to a temporary situation, for that is what it is.

Sit quietly, away from distractions for a while. Take a few deep breaths, sending the breath deep inside you, through your nostrils, along the throat and chest to your solar plexus, the area around your stomach.

As you inhale, you inhale a beautiful calming essence that feeds you in a myriad of different ways.

Just close your eyes for a moment and think of absolutely everything and anything you have learned to do in life. Spend as much time as you can, thinking of things you have done and can do. It doesn't matter how trivial or silly they appear to be to you, notice them and acknowledge them. You may have learned to play a musical instrument, you may have learned to swim. You may have given birth to children or comforted someone in sorrow and ill-health. You may have learned to ride a bicycle or drive a car, and remember how difficult that appeared before you grasped it!

When the images of what you have achieved in your life flow fast, enjoy them. If you get the odd negative image, don't resist it, or fight with it, just send it on its way and think of it as an experience from which you have learned. Start to turn failure into success.

Now, after a few moments, open your eyes and take hold of a pencil and paper or note pad.

At the top of the page write your name in large capital letters and next to it write the date of your birth. Write it out fully — sixth of May, 1947 — or whatever it may be.

Next underline it, and then write a list of all the things you have learned since you were born. Miss nothing out that comes to mind but record them carefully. Just keep going as long as you can and if you can think of something that you consider particularly laudable or a little special, put a star or asterisk next to it.

When you can think of no more things to write down, put your pencil to one side and read through your list. I can guarantee that, if you have been honest in your effort at this point, you will be more than a little surprised at what is on your list. It will not only be long, perhaps very, very long, but it will actually impress you a little. And, so it should, for it is your true "curriculum vitae". This is a little of what you have done and can do. Notice I said a little. Not only will you have omitted so much that you will be able to add, periodically, later on, but you will also realise that, no matter how old you think you might be, there is still much more to come. Whether you like it or not.

What you can do, is to ensure that what comes your way is a positive creative experience as you begin to make life happen for you rather than allowing life to happen to you. It is never too late.

My father was a working class lad who grew up during times of great unemployment in the 1920's and 1930's. He had to provide income through sparring in boxing booths, so that his brother and sisters had food to eat.

A few years ago, this very honest cockney gentleman, having retired as a heavy goods vehicle driver, managed to obtain part-time work as an extra in a television play. Now, at seventy-six, he is enjoying many such walk-on parts in commercials and T.V. productions, and he is loving every moment of this "new" career, that started for him when he was seventy years old!

Life has always some wonderful possibilities in store for us if we but recognise and accept them.

You have wonderful possibilities too, if you will but grasp them.

As with everything in this book, that I ask you to write down, keep it so that it is always available to you either in pad form or upon cards. This achievement and growth list is most important and must be added to, whenever you can think of some other achievement you can claim.

You will begin to see that there is much in you to admire and respect. You can now understand more clearly that you are a precious being, needed and required so much by life.

Without you there would be one less letter-box to deliver to or one less doorstep for milk to rest on, postmen and milkmen need customers, and they need you. However insignificant you feel you are, you are needed and valuable.

Each blade of grass is important to the lawn. You are important to life, warts and all.

At the end of the day on which you read these words I ask you to read and commit to memory the following statement. It will help to mend any battered halo. It will help you to renew a love-affair with the most important person in your world — you. And it will help you to identify with the true reality of what you are — a child of a loving Creator, perhaps temporarily out of step on the Path of Life.

"I am a child of Creation. I have power to be all that I

seek to be. I link with the loving flow of life, and turn
that love to flow through me. And as the love pours
through my heart, I know and love myself deeply and
sincerely. Like the blades of grass in the meadow, I too
am part of a Great living tapestry, important and
needed. I see myself as a true spark of Love, vibrant and
free, glowing and peaceful.
   I choose love and love the 'I' that is me".

   Read this just before you go to sleep. Read it aloud at least
three times now, and then again before you close your eyes.
Repeat the exercise each and every night until you know the
statement off by heart. It will start to change you and your
self-image. I promise.
   We are often perplexed when others don't appear to view
us as we claim we see ourselves, and there are many reasons
why this can be so.
   Usually, what happens is that we wear a masque via our
personality, that we think hides our true feelings, and our
true selves. We literally pretend. For short periods we act out
a role that conceals, or at least it would like to conceal our
true selves.
   When we try to live to another's idea of what we should
be, then we truly have a problem. Likewise, whenever we
build expectations of how another will or should behave, we
lose our flexibility of perception and we start to limit how life
can be for us. We become more and more "hooked" upon an
image that we wish to superimpose upon them, and
inevitably will become disappointed, when, quite naturally,
they fail to oblige and behave to our pattern.
   Our society is geared to the stereo type. My short inside
leg measurement is the tailor's nightmare for God determined
that whatever else I should or should not be, I certainly was
not to be a Fashion House stereotype!
   However, this inability to find well-fitting trousers in any
fashion store in town certainly can attack the ego and I
certainly do not comply with another's image of perfection.
   Unfortunately, we are all bombarded with high pressure

selling that determines what we should be like. It seeks to decide what we should eat, how we should comb our hair, how we should wear our clothes, what house we should have, what new car we need and on and on it goes.

Consequently, we often develop an almost unquenchable thirst for the new, for change, to be better than others, or to have more and more and more and more. We act out lie after lie, creating deeper and deeper unrest within ourselves as we strive and strive.

We look for mask after mask to wear, and then we may be surprised that others do see us not just how we'd planned they should. How dare they! It's their fault! How can they be so dim!

But how can we be so dim?

Man is essentially a loving creature. Given a true unveiling of yourself with all the trappings stripped away, you too are a loving being. Deep inside you seek only to love and be loved and if you are honest with yourself, you will admit that. That is all anyone seeks.

Before you acquire an ulcer or a coronary by acting out a spiralling fantasy linked to someone else's fantasy, stop. And think.

What I seek to show you is the precious jewel that is within you and all mankind. Agreed, it may be a little tarnished and rough, but it is there, none-the-less.

All the techniques and statements I have shown to you are not to help you to build yet another mirage in your life. They are built upon the knowledge that within your heart and the hearts of all men, there exists a pure, unsullied capacity for love that would conquer all hatred, prejudice, fear, resentment, worry, anger, jealousy and hostility and produce a world of peace and joy, health and prosperity for all.

I am helping you to realise and promote the brightest quality you have, the greatest power you possess to bring mental and physical health into your life.

Start being the real you today. You must stop trying to live to another's pattern and idea of what you should be. You will not go out of your way to hurt anyone, that would be an unloving thing to do. But you must identify the true qualities that make up "you". You, and only you, must identify your strengths and talents and you must put using your talents at the top of your list.

If you have commitments, then, of course, it is your duty to see to them, but many of us become embarrassed or afraid and neglectful of our talents and skills. We hide them like the foolish servant. We cower from unfavourable comparison with those skills of another. You must identify your talents and preferences and start to allow them to flower in your life.

It is time to ignore false competition for in terms of health and happiness, competition does not exist. The only yardstick you have by which to live your life is you. There is no other of any value. No guru or teacher will be able to do it for you. Of course, like in all things, they will be able to guide you, but ultimately you have to refine and re-direct your feelings and attitudes so that life begins to flow rather than to jerk and stutter, or stumble into a cul-de-sac of error and frustration.

It is how you grow that concerns you now so measure that and that alone. From this point onwards you are going to nurture your own qualities and share them lovingly with mankind.

LOVING WHEN IT HURTS

Earlier, we looked at the importance of commissioning your body for its daily activity, and you learned to speak to your body, from "Head to Toe", affirming, in a loving way, the positive and powerful efficiency of the wonderful and beautiful structure that expresses "you" in physical terms.

However, it may be that you are experiencing some dis-ease in a particular area of your body, and in such a situation, it is important to direct a little more love and undersanding to the specific region of disharmony, so that healing can then manifest.

First and foremost, you must clear away any misery, and understand in clear detail the remarkable and truly amazing potential of your physical frame. To be ignorant only brings fear and anxiety, so embark upon an understanding of yourself that will lead to a greater awareness and thus a greater love of who and what you are.

Sadly, when we seek to learn more about the structure of our physical bodies, it is often with a view to learn what can go wrong with them and what symptoms certain malfunctions will show.

When I was a student, I had to attend a course of lectures entitled "Health Education". These were supposedly a vehicle for my greater understanding of health and hygiene in a way useful to me when I commenced working as a schoolmaster.

Unfortunately, much of the course was really "Disease Education" in which we learned how to recognise physical disease and to thus see it in all its revolting and gruesome detail. It was one of the most depressing events in my life and I refused to sit through one film, where pain and suffering were being shown as the norm in given set of circumstances and, sadly, there was "nothing that could be done."

Not only is such an idea untrue and irresponsible, such a pattern of behaviour re-inforces the power of disease and conditions us to accept it, in its various forms, as something separate and threatening, over which we can have little or no influence.

Dis-ease is a lack of ease. Just as darkness is simply a lack of light, disease is a lack of health and harmony. It is not a separate and individual reality — it is an unfortunate and sad aberration from a state of loving, peaceful balance in which our bodies should, and would, express perfect physical health.

Remember, we allow disease, we "suffer" it and the time has come for you to stop allowing disease within your sphere of influence, and within your body.

You are going to focus upon health and wholeness and direct your thinking to allow its complete expression within you.

Ensure that you have access to either a book or set of

diagrams, that show the perfect state and function of the parts of the human body. There are many such books available, but take a little care to select one that is clear and simple, and one that has pictures or diagrams that you can relate to easily.

You *do not* need a home medical book that lists in great detail, a plethora of symptoms, and perhaps, graphically, shows to the reader diseased and damaged organs and functions. You need access to clear, positive pictures that instill in your mind the perfect potential of your body, and any particular organ or structure within it.

Now, if you have a part of your body that has yet to express normal, physical health, a part that gives you pain or discomfort, find a picture that shows it in perfect form. If you are not sure of the exact nature of your disease, it is not important as far as this exercise is concerned. For example, in the case of a back problem, see a perfect spine, with perfect muscles supporting it. Where there is non-specific abdominal discomfort without specific diagnosis, determine all the organ functions within the area of the challenge, and look at them all, one by one, seeing their perfect design and their perfect, healthy working.

Should you know the nature or location of the dis-ease, then choose the appropriate healthy and harmonious image to study and concentrate upon.

To begin this exercise, spend time studying your chosen diagram or picture. Study its shape, its colour, its texture. Find out how it works and see it functioning perfectly, doing its work carefully, with a loving strength.

Realise what a good servant this particular part of your body is for you.

Then, when the perfect image and function is fixed in your mind, close your eyes and sit quietly, for a few moments.

Just think what a truly remarkable person you are, and of the great potentials within you. You have at your disposal a physical home of the most amazing potential, seeking to be whole and perfect for you. You are now helping a specific part of you to link with the perfect pattern that exists for it, so that it may reflect its own true perfection in every detail. Reflect upon ideal size, shape, movement, texture with a perfect relationship between all its parts, and a perfect harmony between this part of you, and those neighbours closest to it.

Now see this part of you, working creatively and so very, very effectively, as an integral and important member of the marvellous whole team which makes your physical self.

At this point, see that area of your body becoming full of the Life Force which makes all things. You may see it as light of a blue-white purity, or simply as a gentle, warm pink flow, washed full with spiritual love.

Realise, here and now, just how wonderful your body is and, indeed, just how wonderful that makes you. You are a Divine Machine, capable of anything, able to rebuild and restructure the whole of your being.

Within the quiet of your mind, begin to speak to the part of you which is the focus of your attention. Bear in mind, that just as the stars in the heavens are held in place by Divine Love, so too, will that same love, flowing freely and gently within you, hold all the fibres, cells, atoms and particles of your body in place, doing their perfect work and in a state of complete ease and balance. Disease, pain and inflammation will have no place in such circumstances and thus, they will depart and cease to be.

It is also important to appreciate that every part of your body truly strives to do that for which it was designed, and to do it perfectly. When disease manifests, it is wrong to treat your body like some naughty, disobedient child who is deliberately seeking to hurt and do wrong. Each part of you is always seeking to be whole and have perfect function, to work well for you and all the other parts of your kingdom. It may even, within its own consciousness, feel neglected and isolated in its attempts to do its work, so you must give encouragement and love to it, as you would any long-standing and loyal friend. And by loving a part of your body, you are loving yourself and all creation. For, in a sense, we are all organs within greater bodies, which in turn are specifics within a greater whole. To love a cell of your body is to love God or the Infinite Intelligence which makes all things, for that is where He dwells.

When you speak to your body, do so with encouragement and love. Give it your full support and backing, now, and every day until easement is established and disease has been swept away.

Use this statement:

"I see you perform that perfect function for which you are designed, and for that I thank you. I offer you my conscious, loving thoughts, and send them washing through every cell and atom of your being, bringing peace, harmony and joy as they flow. All ideas of disease are gone and the light of love illuminates every dark corner. You perform that perfect function, beautifully, easily and happily, showing health within every part of you. I offer you my love, now and always, for you and I are one, and so we express that perfect wholeness of being. And it is so."

When you have used these words, imagine your body parts working so well. Feel happy that they do so. Imagine the joy of a body free from disease, a body that expresses only wholeness and complete health. Just think, very briefly of any previously diseased area, being whole and healed, now.

Oh the joy and happiness of such a renewal! And this is your right, and your heritage. It is what your body, each single, tiny part, seeks to express. Allow it to happen, at this moment; let the creative, healing love flow, and flow through you and accept its unifying and vitalising power deep within you.

Then rest in the stillness for a few more moments, enjoying the growing peace deep within your being.

When you have completed this exercise, go about your day, with an expectancy of renewal. Expect things to happen. Expect improvements. Expect healing within you and accept nothing else.

Do not concede to any negative suggestion, however well meant it may be, for disease thrives on a bed of negativity. It is the fertile soil upon which sickness and illness take root and we are seeking to purify the soil around disease, and use a fertilizer that will bring a rather different kind of growth into being.

Sadly, people are often misguided by so-called good intentions. "There is no hope," they say, or "You must not expect miracles." I have often been told that it is wrong to offer those suffering "false hope" that their disease will be healed, when the official prognosis is poor.

But there is no such thing as false hope, there is only hope. All hope is linked to a growing, awareness of man being a truly remarkable being, with unlimited potentials which have barely been tapped. Using Love, which is truly the creative power of our world, hope becomes possibility, becomes probability, becomes fact. When we truly realize who and what we are, then love becomes the ALL pervading influence in our lives and ALL can, and will, be healed.

Prognosis, however lovingly given, becomes redundant as man realises his true nature and commences to unleash this creative power that always has been, is and always shall be within him, waiting to manifest in his mind, body and affairs.

And this loving potential is what you become.

Treat your body as a friend. Get to know him or her well. Get to know all its positive attributes, its qualities, its potentials. Treat it well and give it love, respect and encouragements. Give it kind and loving experiences. Exercise it and then rest it, without placing undue strain upon it.

Give your body a cuddle, a spiritual cuddle, from time to time.

Adorn your body in sensible, health promoting attire. (Don't punish your back with raised heels!)

Cleanse yourself regularly, inside and out, but always gently and lovingly, avoiding shock tactics that will only harm and cause unnecessary stress.

Allow your body to experience variety, without hurting or

humilitating it in any way. Extremes are always bad and to be avoided, whether in diet, dress, or any other form of adornment. Your body is your most sacred companion and you must always regard it and relate to it as such. Treat it with loving respect and great care at all times.

Let your body believe and trust you, knowing that you will not harm it in any way. Provide it with the best and most natural of all things and, most important of all, give it balance of experience. Give it both rest and activity, the rain and the sunshine, the frost and the wind, in equal and gentle measure.

Partake of foodstuffs that are wholesome and as pure as possible, unadulterated and free from refined and noxious chemical substances.

Try to eat mainly food that is in season and fresh, and centre your diet upon food that grows as fruit, seed or surplus to the overall natural regeneration of its type. This may be difficult but at least avoid food, which is the product of over-intensive farming and cultivation — that which rapes and pollutes in its attempt to give greater profit to its producer. That which is the child of polluted fields will pollute your body-temple.

Eat as little animal flesh as you possibly can.

Most important of all, learn to listen to your body. It will tell you what it needs, well before deficiency will lead to pain or disease.

Ask to be guided in selecting the appropriate foods and nutrients for you and those for whom you may prepare meals, and gradually, as you refine yourself and become more alerted to your inner voice and increasing awareness, you will be able to discern, quite intuitively, those things that both your body, and the bodies of others require.

It is worth noting here, that we all have differing needs. Sometimes our own diet will need to change and we can be sure that within a family, no single eating pattern will be entirely satisfactory. For a busy mother, with children to feed, this can be quite a challenge, but when seeking to understand and love yourself and others, the necessary sense of this will become evident and so some flexibility will be necessary.

There is much talk of allergies, and there are many skilled practitioners who can help us determine our perfect diet.

However, there is nothing they will do for you that you cannot do for yourself, and you must avoid becoming anxious about your diet, for that would be destructive and harmful. Be prepared to accept that there are certain foods that will make you strong and healthy and that they are all you and your body really must have. As you progress through the ideas in this book, your eating habits will tend to become increasingly simple.

When considering your diet, commit this statement to mind:

"All food is a gift. It comes from the creative flow of life of which I am a unique and perfect part. My perfect diet is revealed to me in ways that I can recognise and understand. I accept that which is shown to me in a loving, happy way and know that all food is given to me for my good."

Gradually, you will discover that your palate is adjusting, and your preferences will become the correct ones for you, replacing addictions and cravings. In subtle manner, yet clearly, you will come to know what to give to your body as its fuel.

In knowing yourself, you begin to understand that you are your own best resource, whatever situation confronts you.

If a part of you hurts, simply by getting to know it well and understanding how magnificent and wonderful it is, you will begin to love and admire the physical you, in all your splendour, and so initiate the process that leads ultimately to an expression of perfect love and perfect wholeness and function.

In fact, you will become quite wonderfully awe-inspired at just what and who you are, because you are, every part of you, an amazing testimony to beauty and order.

Like a wise, loving parent, you will be moved more and more into making right choices on your body's behalf and the earlier exhortations in this chapter will have become "good" habits.

So now, to recap, remember, identify your talents and give them full expression. Then, give them balance as you allow contrasting positive attributes within you to become more evident in your day to day behaviour.

And as this positive contrast grows, demonstrating an increased breadth of possibilities in your nature for you to use in loving ways, so too can you get to know and love your physical home, your body, eradicating any traces of disease or disharmony within it, as you identify and celebrate its marvellous, intended healthy function.

The more you know of your true creative self, the more you will be filled with happiness and joy at simply being "you."

Get to know yourself. See your true potential in all that you can and will do. Love your body in all its beauty, and take time to bring harmony into your life. It all sounds so simple — "too good to be true" — but for so long we have been conditioned by the negative complications that are essentially man-made misconceptions of our true reality.

You can do anything you can think and believe. It is your right, so take it now.

"Within me IS wonder and majesty.
Within me IS power and love.
Within me are all the secrets and answers
for all that I need to know.
    And it is so."

BALANCING

With many self-improvement schemes and disciplines great emphasis is put upon the need to realise our power to be all that we seek to be, and that is quite correct.

As I have been emphasizing, this is a true understanding of man's natural heritage.

All true, great teachings, have seen that man is really, at his centre, a part of God, a part of His creation — not separate from Him as we often think.

This unleashes enormous possibilities for us as we become truly Infinite in every sense.

With the realisation of all power, however, comes added responsibility. The greater the increase in our influence, the greater is our responsibility to direct that influence effectively and continually for the good of all mankind, and with any programme that enlightens us in this way, there is no going back. That which you have awakened, will not slumber again. If neglected, it may rest for a while but only to stir again later, more dramatically and powerfully than ever before.

This is the nature of disease. Frequently, when we are living out of harmony and we become ill, we are able, through rest and adjustment, to restore ourselves to apparent health once more. In this way, usually, the head cold will disappear, the migraine will abate and the indigestion will be soothed. If, however, at this stage we do not heed these signs and what they are telling us, and we carry on, along our own "Sweet" way, living as we did before, then the problems will certainly re-appear.

Eventually, those lighter problems, become more deep-seated and more difficult to heal, perhaps doing serious damage in our minds and bodies. Here, we have shirked our responsibility and brought upon ourselves problems that could well have been avoided earlier.

Sadly, much of current medical practice is still geared to producing a "cure" so that we are able to carry on life as we did prior to the appearance of disease. We forget that the disease is telling us we have to change, and without change we cannot ever enjoy a healthy life again.

There is no going back to old ways — disease will not allow us to do so. Enough is enough.

You have begun to learn to be more loving and to change your view of yourself, your world and those around you. Even if only a little of this truth has been absorbed into your consciousness so far, it will be like an irritant to bad habits and attitudes. It will not allow you to rest. If you have only read one chapter; one page or one paragraph of this book, your life will be changed, permanently and forever. There is no going back and so you must begin to appreciate one or two other elements of your nature and how you can grow in love.

I used to be a very bad listener. This was not deliberate. It was simply my natural ability as a communicator running riot and not being used effectively and efficiently, so that my relationships with others suffered.

I could have said "Oh well, that is just me. People must take me as I am".

But that would have been both irresponsible and untrue, and a disservice to myself.

In Shakespeare's "Henry IV: part one," the hell-raising Prince Hal was very much concerned that he would appear more impressive as a reformed character in adult life, than if he had lived a good and sober life in his youth. Whilst such a selfish and calculating approach ignores the Law of Karma, in its essence, it none the less touches upon a truth.

We are creatures destined to express balance in our lives, to show contrast in our ways.

If we talk too much, we don't listen enough and consequently, we are perhaps depriving ourselves of valuable information, or not truly to listen to the needs of another.

If we are "good speakers", good communicators, it is imperative to use these qualities and talents with economy, or else it will "blow-out", become dissipated, and hence be de-valued.

By talking less, I became a good listener, and a much better lecturer, counsellor and healer.

To love yourself, you have to give your talents a chance to achieve maximum expression. You have to treat them like the precious jewels that they are and not allow them to suffer from exhaustion and over exposure. Even the most beautiful flower needs to be out of the sunlight for some rest, some of the time.

We need balance in our lives to help this perfect expression of ourselves. In a sense, it is a well-rounded personality that we seek to develop, allowing the loving, creative self to perceive the different facets in these jewels that gleam through your consciousness to their best advantage. A red geranium with a red stem would not convey the same sharp, vibrant beauty as its brother with green foliage.

Within our nature is positive and negative expression, male and female. Psychologists speak of the left brain logical, male characteristics and the right-brain, intuitive female ones. We have to give them both a chance to work together, thus giving far greater power of expression to the individual.

I always feel it is sad that so many men feel ashamed to show those remarkable, deep, psychic feelings usually attributed to women. Equally some women seem almost paranoid when it comes to retaining their feminine traits, neglecting and suppressing the more supposedly male qualities of logic and practicality. The tragedy is that these qualities are simply different sides of the same coin and together make up the currency of a balanced and integrated consciousness.

Looking at yourself for a moment, consider some of the things you find easy to do. Seek out those things that come naturally to you. Perhaps, you are talkative, and you don't allow others to finish what they are saying. Perhaps you are always active, busy, "on the go" as it is called. Spend a few minutes considering all these characteristics and note them down in a column. When you have done that, list their opposites as qualities, their polarities. If you are talkative, for the next week determine to spend more time quiet, listening to others. Should you be always "on the go", take regular time, each day to be still and consider if all your energy is being channelled effectively. If you are quiet and retiring, make a positive effort to take the initiative more often. Cultivate the positive attribute and quality, that is opposite to those you have noted. Since you have moved so far in one direction, you are merely seeking to balance and harmonise the power within you, bringing a greater integration. This will make you so much more interesting and lovable. Others will find you increasingly more pleasant and fascinating, a person to be with, whatever the circumstance. You will become "a man for all seasons." Most important of all, you will begin to love yourself even more. The Divine, beautiful idea that is the real you will be able to shine through more clearly, more powerfully, than ever before. The deep seated love of life that we are designed to be, will flow as an unimpeded stream of warmth and happiness.

Now, tensions will recede rapidly. You are taking the stress from your life, piece by piece, and, like a yacht that was listing badly, you can now sail through life according to how the winds blow upon you. You need never again steer a fixed course.

If your list of characters was a long one, don't worry. Take them one at a time and give them a week each, at least. It would be best to work on the most outstanding and marked one first, but make your way through them, ticking them off as you go.

You will actually find this fun. You will enjoy it so much, especially as you notice the changes taking place in your attitudes and your behaviour. By cultivating the opposites you will be giving a width to your personality that you may not have experienced before. And you will begin to deeply love and respect yourself and others, more and more, each day.

You will gain from this experience as you become aware of ideas, words and possibilities that you missed or ignored before. Others will gain from greater opportunity and experience in your company — it's a double-headed coin, and you will win both ways round.

Remember that you are not seeking the negative. You are not seeking to eliminate or suppress. You are promoting a wider range of qualities, and giving them all a chance to breathe and exist. This simply means that you are introducing true democracy into your life. A fair share for all. You are making space for new vehicles of expression and a richer and fuller life. You are giving yourself a chance to be true and to grow. As you know yourself more, you will love yourself more and more, not as a self-admiration club but rather as a true, caring, loving vehicle of creation.

"I give all the qualities of my soul opportunity to grow. I speak with wisdom. I listen with care. I enjoy good, right action in my life and reflective calm, peaceful moments of consideration. I express balance in all things, integrating all the potentials within me, for a full and harmonious life. Love flows through me in so many different ways. Each day I express new positive qualities of being. As I know myself more, I love myself more and seek good for my fellow man."

PART 8

FORGIVING

One of the most serious causes of disease is man's inability to forgive. Sometimes it is considered a sign of weakness to "let someone off, scott-free" as it is often said, and dogged resentment is frequently condoned and even admired.

"She'll never forgive him for what he's done to her, and quite right too!" How expressions like that help the poison to flow in people's hearts.

Yet learning to forgive others is central to health and happiness. Without becoming a soul who releases others, it is unlikely that you will ever experience a happy, fulfilled life and it is almost certain that you will be storing up for yourself a whole sequence of negative experiences.

We tend to encounter great difficulty in coming to terms with forgiveness, but it is the greatest gift we can ever bestow upon another, and it is the greatest experience we can enjoy ourselves. It is truly a sign of a great capacity for love, to be able to free others, transcend hurt feelings and dented pride, and bear no ill-will towards those who would harm us.

A female aquaintance was very hurt and full of bitterness, because her daughter had been let down, and deserted by a cheating and unfaithful husband. She would grit her teeth as she said, "I can never, ever forgive him, ever, for what he has done." Very soon, three negative, hateful thoughts manifested in her body as cancer. By thinking in such a way, she had begun to destroy herself. The Law of attraction was in full operation as she was attracting that which she sent out.

The shock of the medical diagnosis enabled her to see the need to change her attitudes and to start releasing this man, herself and her daughter, from the bondage of fear and hate. She was able to see the damage such thinking was bringing to pass.

There is a demonstration of great power and great love in

such a transformation, and anyone who learns to forgive experiences a feeling of deep release, as if a weight had been taken off one's shoulders.

Some consider such an attitude to be an acknowledgement of weakness, almost inviting others to trample all over us, since we would appear to offer no resistance. But, in fact, the converse is true. By refusing to retaliate and refusing to accompany others on the slippery slope to unhappiness and disease, we give them no power over us. We begin to take control. Instead of others deciding how we shall think and feel, we react as we determine is good and best.

Instead of being consumed by hate and anger through the actions towards us of another, we choose to forgive and release them.

This is not a pompous "holier-than-thou" stance, but rather a way of living by the truth we were intended to experience and understand. In forgiving, we can glow with happiness, freedom and health, and seek to share those feelings and experiences with all we meet, including those who are the recipients of our forgiveness.

By not forgiving, we are living in the past, attached to experiences we should have grown through, recognised and then left behind.

By not forgiving we are devaluing the present moment, feeling unnecessary guilt over our own apparently inadequate actions and weaknesses.

By not forgiving we are consumed by our need to cast judgements upon others and ourselves.

Krishnamuti, that great man, taught that we should review our day dispassionately, observing how we measured up to challenge and opportunity without blaming ourselves and engendering guilt. Here is true self-forgiveness in operation.

When we forgive, we are setting both ourselves and others free, in ways that we can only just truly begin to understand.

A necessary precept of love is to forgive. A lack of such a willingness implies a desire to have power over others, to wish to restrict, even hurt them. We cannot expect ourselves to be freed from pain and suffering if, in some way or

another, we are not prepared to wish and seek the same for
others.

The Laws of Creation are quite explicit and yet we tend to
ignore them and doubt their value and efficacy.

We live in an environment of cause and effect, that which
is termed Karma in the east — a term meaning comeback. It
is reaping and sowing. That which we give, we receive, only
in greater force and quantity.

The importance of your power to forgive cannot be
underestimated. In choosing to be a loving soul, the need to
forgive will become less and less evident in your affairs, as
you become a channel for love. You will cease to react to
situations in such a manner as to even perceive forgiveness as
necessary.

However, there is a fair chance at this moment in your life,
there is at least one person you feel antagonism towards, who
perhaps, for one reason or another, you dislike and wish to
hold in a state of indebtedness until they have repaid you in
some way. It is also possible that there are those who feel the
same toward you and feel that you have hurt them,
deliberately, through either things you have done, or, just as
important, things you have omitted to do.

Whatever the situation might be, now is the moment for
you to release yourself, and others, and accept the forgiveness that will also be offered to you.

The working of this principle is a truly remarkable one.
Through its operation, obstinate disease of mind and body
can be healed. The more you invoke it on another's behalf,
the more it will also work for you, because it will work
through you. All creative principles and laws do this. As we
forgive, we become channels for forgiveness and this healing
flow touches us at every level on its way to those for whom it
is directed and intended.

There are three points within this law that we must
understand and then put into practice.

First, we must forgive others, and devote time each day to
this act.

Secondly, we must forgive ourselves any shortcomings

and guilts we have accumulated. This is an idea many find difficult.

Thirdly, we have to prepare ourselves to accept and receive that forgiveness which will operate within us, when we are truly "letting-go", and understanding that it is in direct proportion to our own capacity to release others, that we, too, are released.

The sometimes shallow penance in much orthodox religion is both deceitful and negative, and it is worth stating here, that it is only when that deep love within us is truly given freedom, that an act of penance has any true value or effect upon those it concerns. However, it is interesting to note, that, in many predominantly Roman Catholic countries where the Sacrament of Penance and Re-conciliation is widely practiced, the demands made upon psychotherapists are usually considerably less than elsewhere.

We all have a great need to say sorry, and to receive the forgiveness of another, but all too often, we hold back, fearing rejection, and even humiliation. Now, it is time, to grasp the nettle and to let initiative be ours, by seeking forgiveness and making amends, wherever it may be possible.

The Kahunas of Polynesia, a source of much beautiful and simple philosophy, taught that one way to make compensation for any deed for which forgiveness was sought, is to do an unexpected and unrequested good deed for another. This is especially important, in that, often those we have harmed or hurt in some way, may have long since moved out from our lives and it is thus rather difficult to make specific reparation.

From now on, make the following a rule of Life and put it into practice as soon as you possibly can. The sense of release you will feel cannot be overstated.

Be still and quiet for a few moments, and follow my words and ideas carefully.

1. I ask you to think of anyone who has hurt and offended you, and against whom you have some anger or dislike. It may be that there is nobody, in which case you probably had no need to read this book in the first place! On the other

hand, it is likely that there are one or two people you have chosen to dislike for what you feel they have done to you.

I want you to think of one of them now. I ask you to recall their appearance, their voice, and anything about them that will give you a complete and vivid experience of them. I know you may find this difficult, very difficult in fact, but you must persist for you are unlocking so much beauty from within by using this technique.

2. Now understand that whatever it was that they did to cause pain and distress to you, they were simply not being themselves. They were blocking out the flow of true creative love within them, allowing it to become distorted. That which hurt you was not their true loving self and you now have an opportunity to help them. You are taking the initiative. You are assuming control and using your loving power to release them and to let them be free. Now read and say these words:

> "My sense of Oneness with the creative Power that makes all things, grows, moves, and radiates as a light all around me. This inner love touches the hearts and minds of others, and I am protected and loved, secure within its Power. I am cradled in its beauty.
>
> I choose to abandon ways of judgement and criticism. I throw off hates and resentments.
>
> I become a loving soul, as is my right place within the Divine Design, and I forgive and heal both myself and those I meet, expressing the love I feel within me now."

3. In your mind's eye, see those you feel have done you harm. As the warm glow of love wells up within you, see yourself reach out to them. Hold your hands out and see them turn and move towards you, smiling and loving. And in your heart, caress them and then set them free. As you do this imagine a flow of perfect white light as it fills your body, from head to toe and then wraps itself around you, as a beautiful cloak. Those who have hurt you are now cut free, the ropes that bound them are severed and you have demonstrated incredible forgiving love of enormous power.

4. Now, call to mind anything that you consider you have done for which you need to be forgiven. Any deed or act for which, perhaps, you just cannot forgive yourself. Understand that, however badly you feel you behaved at the time, that it was a mistake, in the past, a part of your learning and growing — your growing pains if you like.

You know better now. You will act differently, more positively more lovingly, in the future. It is the "old you", you are recalling. Thank him (or her). Thank the "old you" for teaching you a valuable lesson about yourself, about life, and then let him go.

If you feel you have omitted to do that which you should have done, well, the same applies here. From now on you will seek to act with a loving heart, and you will serve, as a channel for that love. You will be doing that which you must do, and more, for those around you, so that omissions in the form of neglect are unlikely to manifest.

5. Make reparation and compensation where it is reasonably feasible so to do. Be thoughtful and during your meditations (see Meditation and Love) seek guidance for this act. Where it is impossible to make specific compensation, do a "good turn", to someone to whom you are not "in debt". This will unlock the flow through you of the most beautiful, unconditional love on earth.

It is important that you act, that you do something to seal the situation, set everything in motion, and complete the cycle.

It is also important to understand that, from time to time, others may have felt that you ought to respond in certain ways towards them that may not have been correct. They may have neglected their responsibility to consider how they should love you and give you freedom. This is not necessarily an omission on your part, rather an excessive or unfair demand by them.

Love them. See how they too can grow with you, and as you change, so too, will they.

So, then, now mentally forgive yourself.

You too, are released. Any misdeed you feel you have

perpetrated, any neglect, any guilt feeling is broken for ever. You let go. You are free and forgiven. Now say:

"I accept the forgiving love that pours out to me. I welcome it and embrace it. I know that I am forgiven, as I forgive. I am free, and express the loving health that freedom brings, and say thank you for it, as it manifests my life, each and every day".

This is a very dramatic and powerful exercise and, done regularly and sincerely, it will have a dramatic effect upon you. Not only will you begin to feel better, but so, also will those around you. The tension will just flow out of you, and you will wallow in the new, clear expression of love.

I have used the above procedure with many groups and individuals and its impact has always been remarkable. In some instances it has precipitated a chain of growth experiences that have led to better mental and physical health. In others it has unlocked loving potential that has been dammed up for years. Whoever you are, whatever your life experiences have been, this will help you so much.

Use it regularly, as often as you can and feel the growth within you.

Forgiveness moves us into a state of Grace. By forgiving we are telling people that they have no debt to us, that there is no payment to make for events of the past. As far as we are concerned, the slate is wiped clean and they are liberated from the past, completely and without reservation.

This is not to say that we become doormats. The loving power that we generate makes us irresistable and life begins to stabilize and balance for us. Debts of all kinds will disappear. One by one, in some way or another, our material debts too, will vanish or be settled, for within the true creative design of the universe, there is no debt, there is only harmony flowing from a "give and take" attitude which makes allowances for the errors of others, and ourselves.

One young lady wrote to me expressing her great sorrow and anxiety at a large business debt owed to her, that her solicitor felt would not be settled for two years or more, if indeed at all. When using the above principle and sending thoughts of love and forgiveness, a "miracle" occurred and her cheque arrived within weeks.

Forgiving is a "giving in advance". In this most wonderful of acts we are really granting freedom before it has been requested. We are paying money into another's account so that they need not ever be overdrawn and therefore in a negative, debt state, which will eventually express as disease of mind, body and affairs. Some will invoke Karmic Law, the law of cause and effect, reaping and sowing, which so closely governs the actions and re-actions in our world. They may imply that man has to "work out" his Karma by living through experience after experience, often of a painful nature, so that he may understand, grow wise and learn not to do certain things again.

Well, there is a truth here. For every cause there is a corresponding effect. If you put your finger into a flame, it will burn and hurt you, and through such actions, we learn not to do it again. However, the consciousness and level of thinking that needs this type of reproving, is indeed very shallow and fundamental, and through attaining a love consciousness, a state of doing and living for the common good, our perception and intuitive faculties make us a part of causative creation, which is how we were meant to be. As I said earlier, we become causes rather than victims. We begin to enjoy our true destiny as co-creators with *Our* Creator, however we may perceive him. And, despite the teachings of many schools of thought, this liberation is ready for man now, today, not in some distant, far-off day.

As soon as we recognise this, we move into the perfect love and Grace of our Creator, the power of the Cosmos, who seeks only for our good. Within this beautiful experience we become as one with all things, all people, all life and seek only good for them, so that they can share happiness with us.

When we develop an awareness of Karma, then effect follows cause quickly. The results of what we do are felt with surprising speed. The time in which we live dictates that to us at each level of experience. The most positive facet of this is that our efforts to bring ourselves back to health and fullness of life are accordingly imbued with incredible possibilities, the like of which man has not experienced before. In a sense, "miracles" should abound and become more common, if only we would use our hearts and souls to make our world a loving one.

Some believe that until all our Karmic debts have been purged and paid for, we will never be free. Reincarnationists say this will require many lives. Personally, I feel that we would need an infinite number of lives and we would never be free on this basis, for in each life, we would be storing up problems for us to face in another, and then another and so on.

However, some Spiritual Laws are of a higher order than others, and the Law of Grace is such in relation to Karma. By seeking Grace and linking with the Creator of all things, so that we may re-gain our heritage, we enjoy and experience the "truth that shall set us free". Disease, ill-health, pain and suffering are, for me, totally unnecessary and part of a hypnotic race belief that sees virtue in negative states.

True, the pearl, which is beautiful to behold, is the result of damage and irritation to the oyster. But this demonstrates Creation's desire and ability to see all things good and to transform a disaster into triumph. It is no justification to invite disaster and to view it as normal, for that it is not.

Write this statement upon a card and read it frequently, as you work your way through these ideas.

"I live within the Perfect flow of Creation. I am in a state of Love. I see only Perfect ways, and Perfect possibilities. I experience the Grace of my Creator, and I am free. The evil face dissolves from all experience, as good now enters my consciousness, bringing joy, fulfilment, love and peace. In the quiet of my mind, my heart listens and understands. All I could ever seek is mine and I give thanks for its perfect expression in my life."

Remember that you are part of a triangle. You forgive others, you forgive yourself and thus, you also are forgiven.

Your heart can run free through the fields of your soul as life becomes a dance of delight in Love. You are now unshackling your innermost being. Act with sincerity, expect to be free, for that is your right and your heritage, and soon you can see disease and pain leave your path forever as you become a true Lover of Humanity.

And, here, just a word on acceptance.

Many of us are extremely bad at accepting that which is given to us. In fact, sometimes, we may even view a willingness to accept as, yet again, an indication of weakness. We are too big, too important, too self-reliant to need anything from anybody else! — (or so we like to delude ourselves). We pay for everything that we need — we don't avail ourselves of charity!

I remember an acquaintance who had difficulties with his car. The problems were so severe, that a considerable amount of repair work needed to be done on the car before he would be able to use it. Unfortunately, he was retired from work, with little in the way of savings, so he was unable to pay for the repairs.

A friend of his who he had helped in many little ways, had some spare money which was offered to him to enable him to have the necessary work done. She had no family or relatives to give the money to, and she felt it was something she would like to do. She wanted to give; she wanted to help, freely and without conditions.

The man concerned refused the gift. He would not accept it. He could see no "catch" but he felt uneasy about this idea so he refused the help needed, thus depriving himself, and his wife of the use of his car, and also not allowing a friend the joy of helping and giving to him at his time of need.

If only he had realised that his life is a gift. The whole of creation is a gift. We own nothing except that which we truly are. When we pass from this life we certainly cannot take any material things with us, and we also enter this world with nothing but the innate qualities of our personality.

Everything, all that we can see, touch, hear, smell, understand — whatever it may be, is a gift from the power that creates our universe. Our mother and father are gifts, so too are our friends and relatives, acquaintances, and our children — even though, during their disturbed nights we may temporarily feel like giving them back! Even if we were born with a deformed physical body, we must understand that each little thing that we have and experience which is greater than "nothing", is a gift and we have to accept it.

We accept our bodies, at least, for a while until we perhaps abuse it or tire of it, for we may then see only limitations.

But, like other things, it is given to us by our Creator, directly or indirectly. Any blemish or imperfection is a consequence of man's interference with the true flow of life, in some way or another, either at a physical level, or at a mental level.

That forgiveness which others give us, actually comes, too, from the source of all Life, all growth and all love. By refusing the forgiveness of another, we also refuse Divine forgiveness.

"I accept that which I am. I accept all good things as they come from the Creator, and so I accept the Love which builds and restores, so that I may grow, more to my perfect-self within and that I may be healed. And I say thank-you, Father."

The Father here, refers to God, The Infinite Intelligence or whatever it is that you perceive as the creator of the universe. I ask you to identify with Him in any way that feels correct for you.

If you are living your life in a badly damaged or disabling physical frame, I would share a few more thoughts with you.

First, there is little doubt in my mind that man was once able, like some creatures, to regenerate, not only the organs that are being rebuilt, day by day, within your physical body, but also complete limbs, arms, hands and so on. As a co-creator with the Divine, this is a talent that man has lost, but one day he will reclaim this right as he re-discovers his true place as a loving creature in the order of Life.

There is no reason why some creatures should have been

given this capacity and others not. It is simply a question of a lost ability, that we must re-learn. Every seven years, a complete re-building of our physical bodies takes place. Some claim that this renewal occurs every six months. What you have now will not be what you have in seven years time. The pattern is there for you to be perfect, so start rebuilding in a perfect way, whatever your difficulty or problem. Little by little, speak to your body, and as well as blessing from head to toe, do also, encourage areas where there is a deepseated condition to grow as perfet expressions of life, however that may be.

A second point is, to understand that however badly off we may be, remember that even a severely damaged body is still a breathtaking piece of engineering and technology. It is only in its deviation from the norm that we perceive its limitations.

Do give thanks for that which you hve, for it is a remarkable gift. Do forgive yourself if you have ever held thought of bitterness or regret, ideas of limitation and uselessness. These traits are part of a human condition which is lamentable but which man can learn to transcend. Forgive also those that, albeit unwittingly, have underestimated you, perhaps even seemed to patronise you. Whatever you feel, begin to forgive wherever you think that there may be a need to.

Begin to accept that all life is a gift, every experience, every challenge, even though we don't see them as such, initially, they are opportunities given to us for our good. It is our reaction to a situation that determines its nature and the effect it has upon our lives.

You are in control.

See yourself as a child of creation, which you truly are, and start renewal today as you move toward better health and happiness being a loving and forgiving expression of Life.

Be still in the quiet, and say:

"New life starts within me now. Like the Lilies of the Field, I grow, and I am given all that I need. I forgive, I love and I grow."

PART 9

LOVING OTHERS

A friend recently experienced great hurt. He had been accused by a close associate of misleading her and giving her false hope during a very difficult personal crisis. His supportive optimism at a time when everyone else had expressed gloomy expectations, had been thrown back in his face and he was viciously attacked by the bitter, unhappy lady he had tried to help.

He had told no lies. He had simply tried to comfort when things appeared hopelessly bad and his good nature had been abused. To add insult to injury, the good lady he had tried to help, then proceeded to lie to others, accusing him of neglect and disinterest.

Friends, upon hearing about these events, advised him to "sort her out". The general opinion was that she must be confronted and made to stop what she was doing. She should be made to apologise.

However, when he came to see me, he was both surprised and relieved when I expressed a different point of view to those previously offered.

I had experienced a similar situation at almost the same time, I was able to know, quite clearly, what he was feeling.

My counsel to him was to do what he felt was right; to do that which made him feel a warm glow inside him. I advised him to send this lady thoughts of love, and pray that she be helped and uplifted so that she may go forward in life as a true expression of her loving Creator. He also had to forgive her any hurt she had caused him, realising that she was not acting as her true-self ought to do. He also asked forgiveness for any shortcoming on his part, that may have hurt her.

He was able to do this, and to release the lady from his path. He could then get on with his life, freely and happily knowing that he had done all that he could in a positive way.

The situation gradually resolved itself. They became

friends again; she apologised for what she had done and in the whole episode, he had not wasted any energy for negative, hateful purposes. Instead, everything he did was positive, constructive and loving. At the most difficult time he had expressed love — unselfish love, liberating love, which had ultimately overcome all difficulties and problems and it had quietly, yet surely healed the whole problem.

That is loving others.

There was nothing, absolutely nothing to be gained for anyone by being more aggressive, and by creating more tension. There was no healing to be found in beligerent confrontation, only more pain and separation would result for all concerned.

Love in action is setting free. Love is devotion that doesn't smother, but liberates.

"Greater love hath no man, than he lay down his life for a friend".

When Jesus spoke these words, he in no way considered that we should go around, being slaughtered for the benefit of others. That kind of interpretation has been used throughout the ages to induce men to suffer in the name of dubious religious belief, philosophy or some political expedience, without question, on the basis that such suffering and death was fine with God, for it was done for anothers benefit, even profit.

This appalling idea is a tragic misrepresentation and abuse of God given gifts of immense power and beauty. Your body is such a gift, as a vehicle for your life upon this earth. It should be cared for, respected and treated with love, as I have shown earlier in this book.

In a sense, it is not yours to throw away upon another's fancy or whim, to ingratiate their desires. It is yours only to give full expression and opportunity to, so that you become an active vehicle for love. It is the temple of your mind, and spirit, and should be treated as such.

Your life is a gift too. It is a gift for service, and to serve your Creator you have to serve both yourself and others well, in active, positive ways.

The life that you "lay down for your friends" is the loving energy that you can create, day by day, through your thoughts, words and deeds. It is the service that you give to friends, families, colleagues, neighbours and so on, as you make your way along life's path, exploring, and growing as you go, seeking always to help and encourage, to uplift and inspire, to comfort and assuage.

Using energy in loving service is a source of much healing both for those who give and those who receive.

A man with deep seated emotional problems had been writing to me for some while. He had tried almost every conceivable approach to overcoming his difficulties except the most important one. He had not worked at helping those who were in difficulty themselves. Like so many with his type of problem he had not seen the selfish and introverted aspect of his illness, and how true, self-less services to others, would unblock the flow of loving power so that it could flow through him, bringing healing in its wake.

Eventually he saw the wisdom of such an idea, and he took steps to make himself available in such a capacity, a couple of times a week. It proved to be the beginning of his recovery. The love flowed and the love healed.

Human beings are remarkable. In fact, we really have no concept of just how truly special we are, and our potentials are barely understood, let alone used.

We have immense, creative capacities, which, when directed for good, will surmount any problem, and any difficulty. As soon as we throw away prejudice, distrust, fear, guilt and resentment, replacing them with hope, faith, generosity and love, we move nearer to our perfect world, and the Golden Age will be ours for the taking.

And this is perfectly possible NOW.

The greatest teachings command us to love our enemies.

According to my dictionary, an enemy is a "hostile person; an opponent". Yet we are told to love them. How?

First we must re-affirm and be imbued with the knowledge that we are all parts of the one whole. We must understand that every single human soul is linked to us, permanently and for ever. There is a part of you in everyone else and a part of them in you. Just think on that for a moment.

"There is a part of me in everyone else and a part of them in me".

Say this statement to yourself several times, until it truly sinks into your consciousness. As the truth of this idea unfolds, in its simplicity rests a remarkable truth, that will change everything for you.

We are all a part of the creative source of the universe. We are all an expression of God, Infinite Intelligence or the Creator. That quality rests within us, and it is within us all, seeking expression, despite hindrance and mutations, imposed by faulty living, negative beliefs and habits and low group consciousness.

But the secret here, is to realise that when we harm others, we harm ourselves, and when we love others we are loving ourselves.

Take a look at those you may not have liked or cared for. For the moment, be as dispassionate as you can, and try to feel as little as possible; simply observe. Think of them and realise that if you seek to help yourself, then you must help them also. There is no room for hesitation here. You must love them as you seek to love yourself, here and now. You must send them only thoughts of love and wish them happiness and success, knowing that you can share in that too. As they grow, so will you.

Sit in the stillness for a while, and consider those who might be viewed as enemies, or opponents. Now understand, that, in life, there are no really hostile persons, no opponents, certainly not as far as we are concerned. Even the terrorist gunman who shoots in cold blood, must be loved. You probably will find that a tough one to handle but handle it you must. By this time you should be prepared to do so. Even the murderous assassin shares a common factor with you. He too, is a part of God, however twisted and warped he may appear at present. Most important of all, just like you, he too can feel love and be changed by it. Your responsibility is to initiate the process and to begin loving your supposed opponents, those who would seek to harm, hate and hurt, and in so doing you are truly giving him an opportunity to be just like you, for that which is your potential is his potential also. As you grow, so can he.

You will not be abused. You will not be harmed. The power of love is the strongest power in the whole creation. Make that your ammunition, and you will be invincible.

Now read this out loud, three times and then think upon it quietly for five minutes. As you do, picture those who have hurt you, and profess and show dislike of you.

"I have no enemies. The healing power of love flows through me to those who need it most. They are warmed and caressed in its light, and its gentle strength. Hate and fear are dissolved and melt away like snow in the warm sunlight. The Love I express will return to me, enriched and more powerful than before. I am free and they are free now. It is so and I give thanks for it".

When you have done that, once more imagine those to whom you have directed your thought surrounded by a sea of white light. It is white healing light. As this light washes around them, see them transformed, the qualities in them that caused you fear or pain, anxiety or dislike, are transformed to those of friendship and co-operation. Where you once saw hostility, now see friendship. Where you once felt dislike, even hate, you feel love in its place. And remember, that which you do for them, you are also doing for yourself and mankind as a whole, for we all share the same experiences and feelings. We are all one, linked by an invisible thread of brotherhood.

Of course this exercise will require sincere effort. You will almost certainly find this difficult, but nothing worth doing is easy, and you are moving toward better health. You are seeking to claim health in body, mind and spirit, and such a big prize requires a big effort, and demands substantial growth before it can take effect.

Do this every day until you experience changes in your deep-seated feelings about your former "enemies". Until you have mastered this idea, there is actually very little point in going any further.

This must be faced first of all. Until you have truly begun to transform hates into love, you cannot ever be completely healed. Even the slightest residue of hostility will harm you. It will cause tension in your mind and in your body, which, given time, will manifest as disease, perhaps of a very serious kind.

"But, when I can love my enemies, I shall be perfect!" I hear some say. My reply is no. When that is so, you make no enemies in the first place! Most of us have to begin by releasing others and ourselves quickly as part of our growing. In this way people will be less and less likely to form negative opinions of us as we go through life. Wherever a little conflict creeps in, catching us unawares, we can act, swiftly to change the flow from negative to positive, from hate to love, by using the statement before our meditations and, taking time to heal the situation with light.

At this point, it is important to understand something more about your abilities and your power to love.

A young woman lay in hospital and a transfusion was in the air. She had lost much blood during a difficult confinement and emergency delivery, and she was quite weak. However, she did not wish such help and decided to refuse, so that she could get well naturally, in her own way. Meanwhile, two close friends and the husband, prayed for her and sent thoughts of love and healing power to her from their respective homes.

Within a week, much to the surprise of the G.P. and Midwife, her blood count had risen dramatically reading near to normal and she was well on the way to recovery. This little miracle happened to my wife, just a few years ago. The power of love was proved so dramatically, so quickly, and so completely.

Mankind has a remarkable ability and capacity for helping others. When used properly and efficiently, this is a really remarkable talent, one that transcends all conditions, all time and space. We are all able to link, mentally with each other, at any time, and direct thoughts to another so that they will enjoy peace, well-being, harmony and healing. Some would define this as prayer, others as telepathy, but whatever the label that is used to describe such a phenomenon, it is none-the-less real and very powerful.

Many of us can recall, perhaps on many occasions, that we have been thinking of another, apparently quite spontaneously, when the telephone has rung with a surprise call from them, or their unexpected letter has dropped upon the mat. There are literally millions of documented cases of this type of occurrence and those engaged in healing, other types of prayer ministry and medidation practices, will be very familiar with this mechanism resting deep within the human consciousness. Some like Dr Carl Jung, refer to a collective unconsciousness, of which we are all a part, inextricably linked, in a vast network of thought and understanding. Through this overmind, or oversoul, we have access to all knowledge, all understanding, all experience from past to future, since all events in Infinity exist there for us to perceive. This is the record of Akasha to which Dr Rudolph Steiner refers and this is the source from which he claims all his own considerable writings and philosophical ideas emanated, teaching of such magnitude that they still touch the lives of millions through the psychology, educational philosophy, and school of medicine that he founded.

Now, we are all heir to this knowledge and this power. It is not simply the province of a few psychics and mystics, no matter what you have been told or led to understand on previous occasions. Of course, some of us are more attuned to this realm than others, but it is purely a matter of being ready "in thought" or consciousness to accept such an idea, and then, through prayer and meditation, to develop and refine it.

We live at the dawn of the NEW AGE, when man can, and must, take a great step forward as a spiritual being, to claim a new heritage. This is built upon love and understanding, and it will open up man's hearts to areas of perception that have hitherto been closed to all but a few. Man will have access to such much more power.

With this comes a parallel increase in responsibility, to understand the one-ness of all creation, and all mankind. This at at-one-ment. Living as a vital individual characteristic of a much greater identity. It is the microcosm and the macrocosm.

Such an awareness unfolds an understanding which dictates tearing down the barriers of separateness and plunging ourselves firmly in the flow of interconnectedness, of communion and sharing. It is truly becoming a loving soul for love is the cement of life. Such love, a realisation of the Unity of all life, is the "perfect love which casts out fear". At this level of evolution we no longer perceive ourselves as isolate, and therefore threatened and buffeted by life, but rather we engage in thoughts of service and ideas of security. We increasingly understand that our apparent physical separation from all around us is an illusion and that we interpenetrate all things at the more subtle levels of our being. In other words, we are not so much "in the flow". We ARE the flow. We are a vital element in the flow of life's current, and so to, are all our friends, acquaintances, family, and onwards to all life, animal or otherwise.

Here the physical illusion is destroyed. We are really all one being.

This is the spur we need. The idea that to serve ourselves is to serve others, and to serve others is to serve ourselves. When we harm ourselves, and our own life in any way, we also harm others, and thus the converse is true. To cause hurt to another is to hurt ourself, so interdependent are we all.

Service here becomes the keynote for life, so take a few moments to be still and away from distraction to consider the next statement.

"I dedicate my life to service. In all that I do from today, I seek to serve. It is my desire to uplift, inspire and bring peace. I offer myself for acts of true service, and I am alert to every opportunity that comes my way."

Upon reading this you have automatically set silent wheels in motion. You have begun to link with selfless acts of help for others. The more you read it, the more you "volunteer", and in spiritual terms, no volunteer is ever turned down.

Do not mistake service for self-gratifying, public deeds which tend to be the realm of the "do-gooder". No, you are aligning yourself with the true possibilities for help and support here in those acts of kindness and love which can be offered inconspicuously, privately, without demonstrative or theatrical fuss. The supportive telephone call, the caring letter, the late night cuddle to an ailing child, the supermarket trip for a friend, these and a whole range of other small (and not so small) deeds are those in which un-selfish, unconditional love expresses itself. In the words of a song, "Little things mean a lot", and yes, they really do.

There are occasions, of course, as any parent will know, when the best service we can render may appear a little harsh or uncaring. Perhaps the true need is for greater independence and we have to overcome our true feeling, in order to free and let go, as we firmly and yet gently encourage a tearful child to commence school, or an anxious elderly parent to move to a small house.

However, if service born of love is our motivating power, then we cannot fail to do good and promote well-being. Acts of service are powerful ways to show love to others.

Sadly, on many occasions when I counsel those that I help, there is one commonly discovered source of pain.

They may not be "speaking" to someone, when nearly always, the reason for this "silence" has either disappeared from memory or it has been completely distorted and exaggerated, becoming a monster of intimidating proportions.

Whatever the truths in such a situation, there is frequently a deep seated reluctance to make the first move, to take the initiative to break any "dead-lock" that exists between them and the other party.

Are you involved in such a breakdown of relationship, with anyone, either friend, relative or colleague?

If you are, then you must, here and now, take time to

review each situation. You must look carefully at the reasons why you are cut off from another. You will probably find that, in most cases, the original cause of the "fall-out" was really quite trivial. Chances are, that it was used merely as an excuse for giving vent to a vast Pandora's Box of venom, hate and negative feelings. You just happened, to find a handy victim or object for your fears and frustrations. Make no mistake, that is what happened.

However, do remember, that this was not the real you; it was not your true creative, loving self in operation. You were not yourself at all and instead of working to make a disagreement or irritation into a chance to grow, you perhaps saw it as an attack upon you. You had a moment of weakness and pow! You dug your heels in and fell back on your pride.

Perhaps someone chose not to behave how you expected them to and thus they let you down.

Or maybe someone left you out and you decided you weren't standing for that!

Whatever excuse you find, it will be a weak one, and it will be nothing more than an attempt to cover up feelings of fear and insecurity within you.

But now you know different. Now you understand that you have nothing to fear or feel insecure about. You know that you are a real creative channel, a force for good and co-creator with the Infinite Intelligence that makes all things and, of which you are an integral and beautiful expression.

You are going to allow that expression to flow in an even more liberated fashion than ever before, and show the powerful love working through you, touching those around you. You will have forgiven them already, and you will have forgiven yourself. Now, you can take the initiative.

Of course, there will be some circumstances, some situations where, for one reason or another, in a practical way, you will not be able to be peace-maker! The others involved may have long since drifted from your life and perhaps you will never see them again. It may also be true that you sense, deep within, that others who have cut themselves off from you, could not cope with a confrontation, however sincere and loving your intentions are. It is important not to use this as an opportunity to back away, however. Only you can determine whether this is so.

However, in this case, simply wrap them in love, and spend a few moments each day for a week or so, thinking of them as happy and contented, living a fulfilled life, wherever they may be.

Where you can put conciliation into effect, first picture in your mind the individual concerned. Think of how much they might benefit from contact and associations with you. No matter what the situation is, there will always be practical benefits that will accrue from your friendship and care, not the least of which will be your love, which will help both of you to grow as brighter, more powerful vehicles of creation.

Next, you must identify how you will benefit from renewed contact with them. Once again, there will always be a positive aspect for you also, not the least of which will be the probability of more love in your life.

You are actually beginning to "cast your bread upon the water" and you will find it returning many times over.

Now is the time to make the contact, to take the initiative, but before you do so, read this statement to yourself and reflect upon it for a few moments.

"All life is one. I see all created things as important, and I approach them with an open, loving heart. An open, loving heart is a powerful heart. It is invincible. Others return that which they receive and experience. I set the wheels in motion. I heal my life, now, and I heal the lives of others."

Now take action, for without action, faith and truth cannot operate.

It may be that you have a letter to write. It may be that there is a telephone call for you to make. Perhaps it is simply a matter of saying "hello" or beginning a conversation, or it may be that there is a doorbell to be rung.

You will do it. You will do it with love. You will triumph and so will mankind.

There is a spiritual law to understand at this point.

Within all creation there are Laws which give structure and stability. They are Laws which relate to the infinity of all things and it is through these Laws that life has meaning. When we work within the Law in a given situation, life will flow in a relatively joyful and harmonious way, and any effort expended will not appear as such, for such activity will be a delight. Most, I'm sure, can think of some work they enjoy so much, that "time flies" and other work where they are for ever checking their watch. It is akin to these experiences.

So often, we are born with beautiful talents and abilities which are ignored in the pursuit of material and social gain, usually at great long term cost and consequent unhappiness and dis-ease.

There is a Law which says we must ask. It is no use for us to assume that the Infinite Intelligence which created all things, will automatically act on our behalf. That would be a nonsense and take away our freedom of choice.

It is always imperative that we state clearly, and with the whole of our being, that which we seek for our good, and for the good of others. If we ask in this way, always seeking the Perfect, Loving outcome, then we will be given that which we seek. It may be that the answer comes in a fashion that will surprise us, and quite possibly challenge our prejudices and habits, but when a question is asked, a response is always experienced.

We have to be ready for them. We have to be open to opportunity, to follow our hunches, to expect the result without the nature or direction of its manifestation being limited by us.

The dynamic in this Law is conceiving the idea, believing its possible manifestation and expecting it to occur, in one way or another. To complete this cycle we must actually say "thank you" before we are consciously aware of the appearance in the physical reality of that which we seek. We have obeyed the Law, so we have created a powerful thought-form, which then will seek to express in our reality.

It never fails, so long as we then let the whole idea alone and allow the Law to work. We must not block it by becoming over-anxious, thus expressing doubt.

> "Therefore I say unto you, what things soever ye desire, when ye pray, believe that ye receive them, and ye shall have them." Mark 12:24

Whatever your standpoint, I'm sure you will agree that Jesus knew a little about Spiritual Law, and this one is so important.

The statements which you read in this book invoke that Law. They are written with expectancy, and you must read them to first cultivate and then enjoy a total expectancy that will lead to manifestation, a manifestation and demonstration of love in your life, and the lives of others.

As you seek to re-build the bridges between yourself and others, this Law will ensure that you "reap as you sow" and where you send love and conciliation, it will return to you in greater supply. Take the initiative; follow the method, faithfully and sincerely and you will truly move those mountains.

Set the Law in motion by sending love and love is what you will receive.

Sometimes we do have to come to understand an outcome that is not entirely that one which we claim we wished, but we have to allow for the needs of others here.

If we truly love others, then we will seek that which is best for them to occur. It is very common to discover a situation where we have decided what is the "right thing" for another to have or experience, when we don't actually know whether this is true or not. Suffice to say that in our own lives we can almost certainly find occasions when what at first appeared to be the worst possible outcome to a situation, subsequently proved to be in our best interest. In this respect it is always very important to ask for the perfect outcome, without placing limitations upon the good experienced by either yourself or another.

Some time ago my family very much deserved a return

holiday to Scotland, which we view as a spiritual home for us. We could not envisage how this would be possible, for we had little money, and a car which was really inadequate for such a journey. I had imagined which new car we might have one day, but attempts to obtain one had so far met with failure.

As soon as I affirmed the perfect car for my family, we received a completely unexpected cheque which enabled us to buy an excellent estate car, although not the one I had in mind. Within weeks a friend who lived in Scotland called, and invited us to stay for a holiday. When I asked properly, the Law operated perfectly, knowing the perfect solution for us.

In your moves to express love to others, accept that the Supreme Intelligence which creates all things, will know how, and when perfect expression of that love can be demonstrated.

One has to learn patience too!

The greatest learning experience of my life so far, has been to really understand that the true will of my creator is also the true will of myself and that "Thy will be done" really means "my true will be done". In the next part of this book I shall elaborate a little on Perfect Self Expression but it is perhaps correct here to understand that whilst we can know the over-all directions in which our lives can be improved, the precise details are best left to the Creator.

"I am a part of the Intelligence that creates all things. As I seek improvement for myself, I recognise its perfect manifestation, at the right time, in the right place in the right manner in my life. And what is true for me, is also true for others. It is so."

Learn the above statement. Once learned, it will become rooted in your consciousness and enable a quicker, perfect expression of all you seek in your life — health, prosperity, and happiness through the creative Love of Life. Whilst you are learning this, spend a few moments considering any event in your life which at the time appeared to be not in your best interest, but has subsequently proved beneficial. This will quickly demonstrate how Thy will be done is my will be done.

The remarkable truth is that all seeks to be perfect. Even the person you feel you have most disliked, who perhaps appeared to you to be miserable, or unpleasant, aggressive or hostile, deep within has a desire to be perfect. All life moves toward this perfection, impeded temporarily, by the limits placed upon it by an environment polluted with negative thoughts and the deeds which they bring to pass.

As you grow in love, you seek the best for all around you. You will do all you can to help others express love too, and be like beautiful flowers, radiating in golden sunlight.

Any gardner will know that flowers and plants frequently grow perfectly, despite neglect, poor soil, harsh weather conditions and the mass of other challenges that can operate against this happening.

People are just the same. We seek to be perfect and so you must learn to recognise this struggle in the lives of others. Sadly, there is often a battle going on, albeit needlessly, and you must understand your part in this. It is your great opportunity. By sending love you can help to lead them away from the struggle, out into the reality where all fears and hates will be dissolved, their minds and bodies can be healed and they can go forward in life to share the love and companionship of all they meet — including you.

The power of your love cannot be over emphasized. You are not in the business of simply being loving now and again, rather like turning on a tap when you feel you need it, and forgetting about it afterwards. Yours is a building of a consciousness of love that will be with you, every waking moment. Your natural reflexes will be those of love and compassion, of seeking to serve and give selflessly.

Here is an experiment you can try with anyone, at anytime. It is a way of loving another and helping them to be true.

1. Sit quietly, side by side, with a friend or someone with

whom you feel comfortable. Both hold hands and for a moment, close your eyes. Imagine that you are both sitting next to a beautiful waterfall. See the spray rising like a cloud of small diamonds sparkling in the sunlight. This soft spray washes over both of you, making you both feel fresh, invigorated and calm. Enjoy this thought for a minute or two.

2. Feel the cool spray becoming warmer and warmer as it is touched by the Golden light of the Sun. You both become drenched in this warm love.

3. Now understand that this warmth flowing through you is love, healing love. It is the love that restores, builds, creates and forgives.

4. Keeping both eyes closed, ask your friend to "think" or call to mind all the negative feelings and pains inside them and send them upwards to you. As they do this, feel the flow of love as it increases its movement through you, and out to your friend. See this love as a warm colour flowing into them like a soothing, forgiving, cleansing wash of pink, green or white. Do this for several minutes, about five or six or until you feel a release and great peace and restfulness.

5. Finally, imagine, that both you and your friend are gradually wrapped around by this healing light. It is just as if you are both inside separate egg shells which are being filled and washed clean with light and peace. Eventually the egg shells are full and when you are happy with this, let go of each others hand and say a silent "thank-you".

What you have been doing is a form of deep and beautiful healing. You have been giving your love to another, selflessly and effectively. They will certainly feel it and be thankful for it and to make the experience complete, you should do the exercise again, this time allowing your friend or companion to be the "giver", whilst you become the recipient. This is important, so ensure that you do it.

You can also do this quite effectively at a distance. If you wish you can fix a time to link with someone in this way, or you can do it spontaneously at any time.

Always follow the procedure right through. The filling of your "egg" must not be overlooked or forgotten and you must also mentally do this for the recipient of your love, if they are not aware of what you are doing for them. It is simply a little mental and spiritual hygiene, and it is very important, just as washing your hands is good physical cleansing.

You will always feel beautiful and exhilarated after this exercise. The love you have sent will also dwell inside you, as a residue and it will begin to heal you, in mind and body, allowing your spirit to express itself. If ever you know of someone who is unhappy, tired or unwell, use this exercise, with them as the recipient. They will benefit enormously from it, and even if you do not tell them of what you are doing, at a later date they may well offer information to you which will tell you that they experienced something which uplifted and helped them in some mysterious way. Try it and see!

The more that you do this exercise, the more you will begin to live in a consciousness of love, and you will find improvements take place in your mind, body and affairs. Life will gradually appear more positive, more beneficial, more creative, and your love for all around you will be enhanced more and more with each passing day.

As people progress along the path to a consciousness of love, with all its attendant joys, they are more cognisant of a growing inner happiness, rather like a candle that has been lit, never to go out again but to send its warm, bright glow for ever outwards to touch the hearts of all who behold it.

You will smile more. This is a wonderful thing to do for others and smiles are infectious. If anyone is going to catch anything from you, you can do no better than to make them smile. It is a fact that it requires far less physical effort to smile than to frown and sneer, yet we become conditioned to express a countenance of tense, fraught, anger or despair as opposed to the gentle radiance that a smiling face can bring.

You can try another way of loving here. Begin a day with

a decision to smile, gently, as much as possible. Reject the idea of frowning altogether and determine to live the day as a smiler.

Whilst you may experience the odd quip from those who cannot understand the change in you, most will be happier and pleased to be in your company. You will be nice to be with, and the smile in your face will be reflected in your mind and your body. This smile will permeate every part of your being and will open the doorways to better health and happiness. Turning on a smile, making a smile a "conditioned" response is part of a re-education, rather like the flicking of a switch. Rather like all thought, it opens the channels for the positive loving power to flow through you, generating so much goodness.

There is nothing false or insincere in this idea. In fact you are merely "setting out your stall", making a declaration for all around you. You are becoming a more loving being and your smile will be your calling card.

No "Cheshire cat" grin is called for. It is rather a changing of habit. You may have become addicted to wearing a miserable expression upon your face and now you are changing it. For good.

Cultivate the smile, and wear it when you are in neutral or going forward and then you will be able to call upon it in adversity. It will be your magic wand, for use in casting a beautiful, loving spell on those around you. No one can smile too much.

Remember, always, that of all the gifts you can give to others, "the greatest of these is love". You will be a giver and transmitter of the most perfect signal in the whole of Infinity. You are on the winning side in the game of life, so play up, and play your heart out.

Love defies expression in words. Love is an experience. That cuddle which surrounds you, and is a true embrace, pours its perfume over you until you are immersed in the experience. There is nothing you can say or write that would explain the expression of self-less, unconditional giving, which true love surely is.

This is what you give to others. You are offering others the most beautiful experience they could ever have, as you let them imbibe in its limitless supply.

You seek that which is best for others, and that is true love in operation. That is your sole desire.

You are also making a beautiful, positive choice here. You are choosing to love. You are making a conscious decision and there is no going back.

You are choosing to determine your attitude to people and situations. Others will not make you angry or sad for you can decide how you are going to respond.

I remember the story of a man who was verbally attacked, in front of a large group of people, by a sad, and angry stranger, over some very unimportant issue. He refused to retaliate but simply allowed the stranger to finish, and then smiled at him gently and moved away.

Later his friends rebuked him, saying how weak he had been not to react, and to give as good as he got. Why, he was not even angry!

The man replied, "Why should I let another decide how I am going to feel? If he had offered me his love, I would gladly have accepted it. Instead, he offered me his anger, and that has no place in my heart".

When you offer others love, they will gradually respond to it, one way or another. Here was a man, well centred in that love, who decided that he was in charge, and in control. That control was based upon the power of love, and its ability to reject all but itself. No one was going to decide that he should feel angry.

As you choose to send out love, you offer others the greatest of all possible gifts. You offer them an opportunity to see as you see, to feel as you feel, and to know love, as you know love.

"From today, I choose love. I choose to give love in my thoughts, words and deeds. All of life is based upon love, as it flows out to others from the centre of me. I choose love and I share it with the world."

PART 10

MEDITATION AND LOVE

In recent years, meditation has become increasingly popular. There have been many schools and organisations offering a range of benefits to students of their particular approach and, indeed, this can sometimes be the case.

There is no question that a regular, daily practice of a meditative type will bring to the student new, fresh insights into life, and a greater sense of inner peace and well-being. This in turn may show as increased creativity, happier disposition and a diminishing requirement for drugs, alcohol and tobacco. And everyone would agree, I am sure, that such changes can only bring good into our lives and bring us nearer to the health of mind and body we all so desperately desire and seek.

However, meditation is also very misunderstood. Some regard it as a purely medical tool. Others cloud it in mystery and esoteric and religious jargon, and interesting though this may be, it can limit the experience for the seeker if it doesn't deter him altogether.

Essentially meditation is both these ideas, and more.

Meditation has the same root as the word medical, meaning to heal and at once one can see that meditation is a wholistic practice. In other words it is a restorative, unifying, making whole, process and is thus important to anyone professing the desire for good health.

However, it goes a little deeper than this idea, for we are only scratching the surface.

Meditation is really an attempt to go "within" to find our source, our creator and to perfect our relationship with Him, however we may perceive Him*.

Now, our true relationship with our God or Creator is one of Perfect love. When we identify with God, we identify

* The word Him is used as my stylish preference. Her or It would be equally meaningful.

with love, for that is what our creator is and it is love that is the basis of all true creativity and harmony. Therefore, when we seek God, we seek love, or conversely, when we seek love, we seek God, for the two are the same, and it is only in such a union that true health, wholeness or "holiness" can be expressed. Anything less is temporary at best.

When we are out of harmony with our Creator, and when our relationship is impaired because the "God in us" is not being expressed, we manifest fear and anxiety, which, in turn, alters our magnetism so that we may then become ill or diseased. To get back at ease, we have to get back into God. It is this feeling of unison or at-one-ment that is the "perfect love that casts out fear". Fear is merely an expression of our separation from the Divine, and through meditation we begin to attune more and more perfectly, so that fear becomes redundant in our lives. It is then a clear pathway for the easement to take place at every level of our being, so that health and prosperity are ours.

During the following pages we shall make a journey into the meditative experience so that you can move into that loving expression that we call God. It is worth recalling that all intuitive experiences depend upon love for their existence — any mystic or experienced psychic will tell you that — so the intuitive, limitless expression in your life is structured upon the same idea and manifests through the same channel, and that is love.

Before any truly meditative time, it is imperative to relax the physical body. There are many ways that this can be done and it is really a question of finding that which will suit you at any particular time.

First of all, you "set out your stall" and make it perfectly clear that you seek to link with Divine Love, with the true creative power of the Cosmos, from which all knowledge and goodness emanates. So you link with this statement.

"I identify with love and offer myself as a vehicle for its work upon the earth. I attune to all ideas of purity and goodness, and I am wrapped and sustained in Divine Light."

As you read this to yourself, imagine, very briefly, that you are sitting under a waterfall of beautiful, white energy, that washes all around you, forming a coat of light on all sides of you. It is important that you do this at the beginning and end of each meditation and prayer time. Just as we have physical hygiene, we need mental and spiritual hygiene also, so make this practice a habit. Remember that this energy, glowing white with a radiant purity, surrounds you on all sides; in front of you and behind you, above you and below you, to the right of you and to the left of you. You are secure in its care, as it washes away any negative thought and ideas of life that may have influenced you a little in your day to day affairs.

Now, before you meditate, here is a little checklist to observe. It is an ideal which you should aim for, understanding that there may be times when it is difficult for you to adhere to every point, all of the time, as for example, when you are away from home on a holiday or on business.

Nevertheless, it is useful to understand meditation as a discipline to be learned and practised, even through the difficult times as well as the good ones.

1. Select a time that you can generally sit quietly for a few moments each day. It may be that the evening is best, as it is for most people, although one should aim to spend time in the stillness at the start of your day also. Never meditate after eating.

2. Choose a place for meditation that is not used for noisy, boisterous activity. If possible, create your own little sanctuary in the corner of a room which you can dedicate to your quiet moments. Adorn it with flowers or a beautiful picture.

3. Always discard working clothes. Find some loose fitting cotton clothing for use especially in meditation.

4. Wash your hands and face beforehand, if only as a

symbol of your cleansing of yourself before attuning to the flow of love.

5. Never rush into meditation or try to contain the experience within a limited framework. You will be able to determine the length of meditation to suit you, over a period of time. It will vary, but will probably settle between to 20 to 30 minutes, with some periods being a little shorter or longer than others.

6. Sit in a comfortable, upright chair, keeping your feet upon the floor, preferably without any shoes on. Your head should be erect, your back straight but not still and your hands resting lightly upon your lap.

7. Ensure that you will not be disturbed for a few moments.

8. Say your opening prayer, linking you with all purity and light and offering yourself as a vehicle for the love of your creator or God or however you understand the Infinite Intelligence, as you imagine yourself under your fountain of light.

9. Place a small lighted candle near to you positioned so you can see it without straining.

You are now prepared. You are now ready to relax for meditation, so close your eyes and direct your thoughts to your feet and toes. Think of them and the wonderful service they do for you. Even if they do not always work as well as you feel they might, thank them, give them your love and then let them relax.

Next, move your attention to your calf muscles. Thank them, give them your love and let them relax and enjoy a deserved rest.

Now focus upon your thighs and hips and express your thanks and your love for them, telling them they deserve to rest and then let them relax.

Continue this procedure, carefully and slowly working along your spine and the muscles on either side of it, spreading out across your abdomen, stomach and chest, thanking, loving and relaxing.

Then spend a little more time giving peace and love to your shoulders, neck and arm muscles. Tell them to lay down any burden and to be free, as you love them and thank them and let them dissolve away into relaxation.

Focussing upon your hands, thank them also for helping you so much, and then let them go, and let them relax, giving them your love.

Finally, scan your attention across your face, and your scalp, paying special attention to your eyelids and your jaw. Let them know they are loved and appreciated, very briefly, and then let all the muscles in your head relax and be still.

As you do this, you will probably experience a warm glow around your eyelids, that you can once more direct all over your body in waves of beautiful calmness, caressing each part of you as it moves. This is the beginnings of a loving flow through, which will release tensions and anxiety as its power is made more and more welcome and its effects intensity.

Now take a deep breath, without straining, inhaling deeply and directing the flow of breath through your nostrils, passing your throat, your chest, and into your abdomen, as your abdomen rises like a pump. Hold the breath in for a while, and as you do so, feel the rib cage and the chest also expand to receive its goodness.

Then release the breath, allowing it to flow out very slowly, the slower the better, until all the breath is gone.

In the stillness, enjoy the stay of breath, that moment between exhaling and inhaling when all is still, and all is peaceful. Savour it, taste it and enjoy it. During that time you are in the loving peace that "passes all understanding". Tension is released and consciousness rises. Repeat this deep breath twice more.

Now allow your breath to settle to an easy, gentle rhythm, as it moves in and out. Perceive your breath as the gentle loving life flow that it is. It is offering itself to you in its unsullied, pure form, for you to use in the sustaining your life. This is a truly wonderful fact. You are the recipient of such unconditional love from creation, each and every day of your life. It is given freely and lovingly. Think of it as such.

Your in-breaths are flowing to you in an unending, abundant supply, freely and lovingly given by your creator. The best things in life are really free!

Mentally give thanks for your breath, and then transfer your concentration to the lighted candle. If your eyes are heavy and comfortably closed at this stage, as they may well be, then see your candle as within you, in your minds eye.

Your candle is you.

In the centre of your candle is the wick which burns with the purity of God's peace and love. That light now burns within you as you glow and shine in the stillness.

See the candle flame within you, steady and beautiful. Now use this affirmation and say it to yurself, quietly, over and over again, slowly and deliberately until the words fuse together and dissolve into the beauty of the idea.

"I am the light of the world.
I am the light of the world.
My flame burns bright with love and with peace and I am now love in the world".

Enjoy the stillness for as long as you feel you wish to, and then begin to make your journey back to normal consciousness in the following way.

1. Gently focus upon the image of your candle, at first simply mentally.

2. Gradually, as slowly as you can, allow the light to enter by slowly opening your eyes, just at a squint at first, directing your attention to the flame of your candle.

3. Open your eyes wider, little by little, becoming aware of the extremities of your body, your hands, your feet, your face and legs.

4. Begin to clench your hands, and wriggle your toes, and then take another deep breath, as you did at the beginning of your meditation. As you breathe out, be aware that meditation is both a giving and receiving process. Although you receive at very subtle levels, and may not be aware of your benefits at the time. Say a gentle "thank you", silently if

you wish to complete the experience and then slowly stand up, stretching your arms upwards and anchoring your feet firmly upon the ground.

What I have offered to you here is a platform for certain meditations. It is important to understand that there are many ways of raising consciousness and receiving your God-self whole heartedly into your being, for that is what meditation is. It is possible to use musical sounds, repetitions of various kinds, strong, powerful mental imagery, either the spoken word as in a mantra, beautiful ideas, as in flowers, where God's lavishness is expressed so wonderfully, and the most effective ones tend to be powerful words and powerful mind images.

You can determine the details best for yourself, but always dedicate yourself to love, whatever approach you use, and align with wisdom and truth. The gold of wisdom is symbolized in the gold of the candle flame, we have used here, and the words of our repeated invocation, associate us with the creative, loving flow of life.

From this point concentration you will experience many different things. Your mind may appear to wonder at first, perhaps considerably, but don't worry about that. Always gently direct your thought back to the candle and the words of your invocation and you will reach the levels of meditation where the thoughts come from within rather than without.

The flow of meditation will then take you around the new ideas and experiences as you become further raised in consciousness and contemplate that which you receive. This is a truly creative state where you will gain fresh insights and "new ideas".

Finally you will move to a state of "at-one-ness" where your sense of individuality will be merged with all creation. You will no longer experience any feelings of separateness and you will be happy to simply just "become what may". Here you will wish to give thanks for just being you and a part of all things as it is at this stage, sometimes called "Thanksgiving", that healing can truly occur. It is a wonderful experience and your life will grow so beautifully, the more you touch your God-self at this level.

It is the Divine within us that we reach in meditation. It is the God expressing as us. We leave the illusion of our separate, and even isolate physical lives behind as we become once more linked with our true selves, that incredible, omnipotent "us" the "imprisoned splendour" that can solve all our problems and assuage all our fears. Here we touch the Heart of God and experience perfect love. Fear and anxiety dissolve, they melt away, for that "perfect love which casts out fear" is the growth of understanding deep within that WE ARE God and that, if we let it, the God within us will express through us in beauty and in love, each and every moment of our lives.

This is true healing when we can realise this, not as an intellectual concept, but as an experience, day by day, moment by moment, then we are surely claiming our birthright and "going home" in every real sense. We become powerful channels for love, and bring "Heaven on Earth" closer with each passing moment.

Read this statement now and absorb it.

"My Real-Self is My Creator expressing through me. I am Him and He is me. There is no separation, only unity, and it flows as love in my life. I send out loving thoughts to the God in all my fellow men, to the birds, and animals the flowers and trees, to all the world and all creation. This is Perfect love, fed to me daily in endless supply, and as I share love and give love, it grows, allowing Heaven to establish here on earth.

And I heal the earth; and I heal all things and so, too am I healed.

And it is so".

Learn this so that you can think it and say it at any opportunity. Practice the presence, as you would practice the piano or harp, for it will become as music in the deepest recesses of your heart.

Remember at all times, that meditation is the greatest

opportunity for the infusion of creative love, and that meditation is not another form of prayer.

In prayer, we tend to be petitionary in that we are asking, or rather seeking to take the initiative. The meditative state is very different to this. Your line of communication to the Infinite Intelligence is refined and opened so that you can receive love, and the help and guidance that love can bring so that harmony may be established in your life, mentally and physically. In true meditation you seek only God and then you listen.

Your spiritual awareness is heightened and your receiving station is operating at the right frequencies for input from a higher source to register freely and effectively.

It is rather inappropriate to refer to different types of meditation. There may be differing points of focus beforehand, but meditation is not for any particular purpose other than to allow the expression of God more closely to manifest in your life.

This, of course, means health, as well as happiness and affluence, for creation is all these things but they are the outward signs of this manifestation, rather than the manifestation itself.

We should never start our meditations with demands or purposes, for we are limiting the possibilities of such a beautiful and magnificent union.

If we have a purpose or need or request, we can of course voice it before a period of silence but that must never become a "condition" for meditation. In truth, we should use the loving power that flows into us for healing and so on, after we have been "in touch" and still. Otherwise we are saying, "I'll love you if you love me", and that simply erodes the depth of experience we will have, for in so doing, we question our belief and knowledge of the power of creative love.

Love is the greatest protector in the Universe; it is the greatest power there is.

During a meditation we are showered with that love, so deeply and so completely that we begin to accumulate a form of protection that, in time, can help us to triumph in the most difficult of circumstances. Challenges will become opportunities and chores can be transformed into delights. This is so true, and given a fair trial, as with all things, you will be wonderfully surprised at the attributes of Divine Love that you will express and demonstrate in your life.

Others will notice the changes in you. You will cease to be drawn into negativity, conflict, anger and panic. Instead, you will remain calm in difficulty, seek conciliation at all times, and peace will be the major facet of your outward appearance. You will be the one to be called upon in a crisis, for you will know what to do, and you will do so in an effective and caring manner.

The reasons are simple. The channels for power within your physical frame will be unblocked by the new, loving orientation of your thoughts and feelings. You will truly be master in your own house and others will know it so. So will you. You will, in fact, be expressing the real you, more and more as time goes by. You will be approaching that Perfect Self-expression.

And that is where true healing lies.

We each come to this life with a unique role to play. Nobody else can possibly do what we are here to do. Reflect upon that for a moment.

"I am unique. I have a role to play, that is perfect and right for me, and I am given all that I need to accomplish it."

Your unique quality is so important. It is why you are here. Nobody can take your place. Every breath you take, every thing you do and say, has a permanent effect upon creation. You have made a good start at bringing "right action" into your life by centering upon love as the source for all you do. Love is becoming your motor power, your fuel.

Perfect Self-Expression is available to each one of us, for we only have to ask, and the way will be shown to us.

"Ask and it shall be given unto you. Seek and you shall find".

We have to be prepared for change, but the change will

always be of a constructive kind and I emphasize, there is nothing presented to us that we cannot face and overcome with confidence and success. Change is necessary for most of us for we have usually strayed so far from our intended path in the world. And sometimes it will come quickly.

But the nature of Divine Law is such that we only face given situations at the time and place that is best for us, and this is also where meditation comes in.

Meditation helps us to grow and serve, and to attune to the whole of creation where the secrets lie.

In meditation we open ourselves to the source of all possibilities, which manifests within ourselves. The knowledge we need to direct our lives is "added unto us" when we truly seek for the good and the loving to flow through us and have expression in all that we do. Meditation enables us to become more and more refined and sensitive to that inner voice which will always seek to enlighten, unify, heal and harmonise.

We become receiving stations for the voice of our creator, and, given true, sincere, and regular opportunity, we will be guided without error, along the way that will reconcile us once more with our role in the plan, so that our lives once more become purposeful and encased in a meaningful flow of actions and experiences.

In the loving flow of meditation, we strengthen our link with our true selves, our Divine or Infinite Self, that part of us, which knows the way forward both in the minute, day to day details, and in the larger, more expansive direction we are here to take.

Our meditations enable us to "earth" the love which builds and creates, and is always seeking to wash away all disease and pain, all suffering and disharmony, and to establish balance in our minds, bodies and affairs.

Anyone who has already opened themselves, begun to listen instead of simply talking and thus brought a true dialogue with their Creator in their lives, will already know that peace which can, and will enter and touch them in such a gentle yet powerful manner. It is a truly moving experience, and one is never the same again.

I remember teaching one lady how to approach her meditations, and so allow the light to flow through her. She had been very troubled and her life was, to say the least, full of turmoil and uncertainty. Her confidence had gone and she felt that her life had become meaningless. Every task she faced seemed terribly daunting and awesome, and she could not see how she was going to cope.

By becoming completely relaxed, and focusing her thoughts upon the flow of the Loving light from the Infinite Creator, she began to feel washed and cleansed of all anxiety, which was, after all, only a sense of detachment from God.

As the light flowed through her, she felt so peaceful, completely safe and at one with life. She was realising that, come what may, all would be well and that in the Silence she would be recharged and advised sufficiently to meet the tasks of her day.

Her problems didn't vanish overnight. Her awareness of possibilities, and her ability to deal with life effectively grew and grew as she realised that she and her Creator were essentially one and the same, and all she had to do was to identify with the loving flow of his breath, be at one with him and give love a chance to work in her and through her. Mountains became molehills, and challenges, opportunities. The Divine Design had started to work in her life, healing was taking place, and she moved closer and closer to Perfect Self Expression.

Remember that the true, unconditional love is Perfect and without blemish or tarnish. When moving through matter, that matter will automatically respond to it by seeking to demonstrate the Perfect Pattern within its consciousness or mind.

As love flows through the cells of your body, they will wish to express love and only love. They will seek to be healthy; they will be able to do nothing else. In this way disease can and will simply dissolve and melt away, becoming an idea of the past.

Your mind will be washed clear of impurities, so that the negative emotions, which enslave us with fear, dread, jealousy, hatred and all those other features of insecurity, will be diluted progressively until you will not identify with them any longer; they will jar upon your consciousness when recalled, as unwelcome visitors, and you will immediately re-align to those ideas of loving and serving which are really your true nature.

You will be able to think more clearly for there will be less "clutter" around to prevent you for being part of the creative flow. It is certain that you will not only wish but also, need, to serve others regularly and unselfishly, each day of your life.

Spiritually, you will be aware of a great sense of purpose for you and all you meet. Life changes for those who meditate and centre their thoughts in love, so that it becomes a meaningful and joyful sequence of learning opportunities to be cherished and appreciated, to be savoured to the full.

Most important of all, you, the dedicated student of loving ways, will be protected from the "slings and arrows of outrageous fortune". You will be surrounded by the strongest Power in the Universe and nothing can ever touch you or hurt you again. When you are truly flowing with love, the Law of attraction will operate to that effect, bringing to you that which you give. Those who harm you would be powerless so to do and they, in time, will be impressed and changed by you, for they will want to get "in touch" too, and find this fountain of love.

I heard a quote the other day, attributed to Lao Ste, a Chinaman of 6 B.C. He said, "The Human Spirit has its source in the Divine Fountain, which must be permitted to flow freely, through man. Anyone who flows as life flows, has solved the enigma of human existence. This person needs no other power. Everything is healthy which flows with the Universe".

If we flow with the creative love of life, we will be healthy, of that I am sure. It is when we block and hinder that flow, that we are ill.

Through love and meditation we will learn how we are to achieve just that. We are taught how to love.

It is now generally recognised that during meditation, when the brain records Alpha rhythms, the physical body is repaired at an extremely efficient rate, and in medical circles it is often offered as a "therapy" to help those with serious physical problems. This is simply because the body, with the negative influences of mind subdued, is liberated and able to return more quickly toward its perfect state. There is no pill or potion that will do that for you.

Of course, medications can help in many situations, to support life whilst healing takes place, but all healing comes from within. The resources we need are available waiting to be tapped, without side effect or painful dependency, and the power of spiritual love can be felt at every level of being, including the physical, just as a drug can be. In a sense, it is the truest kind of "fix" we can have — free, unlimited, harmless and permanent.

The patch-up repairs we experience on a day-to-day basis never, usually, deal with the true cause of our poor health. They are often cosmetic and without the necessary inner changes, they are doomed to failure. The disease will re-appear in the same or another form, but return it will.

Use meditation and love as your potions. Take them every day, regularly, and accumulate a balance of healing power within you.

Meditation is accumulative. Its frequent practice is a builder of the most impressive kind as you will discover. In your petitions, offer this prayer.

"Teach me the ways of Truth, to love, to serve, and to heal. Bring me closer with each moment, to the flowering of Peace within me. That I will be a light for mankind, to see clearly the ways of perfect Harmony in all the affairs of the world.

I show love and I give love, offering my heart in its beauty to Thy Will, knowing Thy Will is my will in Truth."

At all times remember that the Will of God or your Creator is also your will. It is only when we are "out of sequence", that we cease to live as our creator would have us do, and, as we are an integral part of our creator, to be as we really wish to be.

When we are diseased, our creator is diseased. He cannot express wholeness, while we do not. Our pain is his pain. Our sorrow is his sorrow also. He cannot totally express perfection until we do. That is why, by getting back in touch through our prayers, and meditation, and with the affirming and identifying of love in all we see and do, that we move nearer to his plan.

Each one of us is so important within the Plan. Without you, the tapestry is incomplete and cannot be viewed in its true splendour. You are a part of the weave of the fabric of life, and it needs you to be strong and effective, fulfilling your potential and demonstrating all your constructive and creative qualities. You are now well on the way to success.

"I now show the Divine Pattern in my life. Perfect expression of my true potential now flowers and comes into being in all my affairs. And it is so."

Learn that statement and use it frequently. Say it at every opportunity as you seek to fulfil your destiny.

Man has reached for the stars. His creative search of the cosmos had led him to seek outward pathways to other worlds, to new knowledge and ideas, to realms the like of which he has only dreamed before.

And yet, the most beautiful mystery rests within him, along with all he ever needs, or seeks to know.

Continue your search as you peel away the layers to reveal your "imprisoned splendour" with all its beauty and power.

The answers are there, waiting for you to find them and the journey is the most wonderful you could ever make.

You are going home. That is where love is. It is waiting for you like a patient, long-suffering friend. Greet it and hold it fast, and never let it go.

PART 11

LOVING TO LAUGH

I met a man once who was a marvellous after-dinner speaker. He had the gift of producing laughter and happiness wherever he went, and so he was always in great demand. People knew they could rely on him to relate many stories, illustrating how he could see the funny and humorous side of life. His turn of phrase was truly wonderful, and his powers of observation were remarkable. He could see the humour in all things and obviously loved life immensely.

A sense of humour and the ability to laugh and see the fun in life are great healers. If you truly love something, you will be sufficiently secure and mature in relation to it, to see its amusing qualities.

This after-dinner speaker once stood up to address a group of people at a function, his facial expression was straight and unsmiling. He said that he had recently seen his doctor, and that he had "Everything going for him." He continued, "My doctor said, 'yes, your eyes are going, your hair is going, your teeth are going . . .'"

The assembled group were reduced to loud laughter so very quickly and laughter can be a great, great healer, showing a free flowing love of life.

I'm sure that you can recall situations where the tension was released, potential problems were diffused and attitudes changed by laughter.

Sometimes, of course, laughter can be provoked by a cruel idea. It is possible for people to laugh from embarrassment or fear, or extreme anxiety.

But the laughter that is from the heart and makes the stomach tremble and vibrate, is a different proposition entirely. It is loving life. True joyous laughter is very different from the cynical snigger.

Science has proved that the tears of laughter actually have constituents of a different type to the tears of pain and sorrow. It is truly a beneficial and health promoting practice.

On a sunny day, people tend to smile more. The sun uplifts and inspires us, and takes away our gloom and despair.

It is a fact that when we smile, we begin to change the way that we feel. In other words, if we cultivate a smiling habit, it will influence how we feel. As you smile you project different light, different energies, and these eventually effect every part of your being, every level of your consciousness.

I remember once that I had to drive alone to tackle something I did not wish to do. I decided to smile and to bring memories of happiness into my mind and it worked a treat. The journey and occasion passed without any problem and I felt relaxed and happy. For when we smile our facial muscles are more relaxed, less tense. We really use far less energy in smiling than we do when frowning.

Try it for yourself. Clear your face of any expression for a moment and tell your face muscles to relax and be still.

Into your mind, very briefly, draw a memory of an occasion or circumstance that has worried you and filled you with concern.

As you do this, you will experience a tightening of muscles in your face, as a worried frown develops like a mask of despair.

Now wipe the memory from your thoughts. As you do so, once more, tell the muscles in your face to relax. You will have to do this, for even though the memory or image has gone, there will still be a residual tension in the muscles. This will illustrate just how we can, over a period of time, accumulate excess tension and stress in our physical bodies, causing pain, disharmony and disease.

When your face feels relaxed once more, think of a happy event, a really joyous and positive experience, that you can recall clearly and vividly. Remember everything that you can, in great detail, and re-live the occasion in your imagination. Whilst you are doing this, your face muscles will naturally begin to produce a smile.

Don't try to resist it, but encourage it to spread and spread, as if the sunlight of the dawn were gradually radiating across a landscape, bringing a feeling of warmth and contentment in its wake.

Very gradually, you will feel transformed, as this simple idea influences not only your face, but gradually filters right through the whole of your being, for when your face smiles, your whole body will follow suit. You will begin to smile all over your body.

Every cell within your physical being will imitate until you can "feel" the smile everywhere, deep within you.

The true beauty of this exercise is that you will feel how you are using very little energy to smile and in fact, you will be opening yourself to a more relaxed flow of the loving power that always resides in you, just wanting to be summoned to the surface by your thoughts and attitudes.

When you smile, you open the door to health and happiness and begin to feed a new response into your own body, and also to the people around you.

A truly smiling soul not only allows his own light to shine more clearly and more brightly, but also sheds more light upon the people and situations around him.

Cultivate a smiling habit. There is no need for a cheshire cat grin here, for that will fool no one, especially if it is purely masking a negative emotion.

Take the "squareness" out of your expression — "round it up" with a smile.

Start your day with thoughts of Happiness and use any device that will help you. Of course there will be days when you find it a little more difficult, but bear in mind that the whole purpose of the book is to make you the centre of your world, so that you cease to react to life, but rather make life happen from you outwards. You are taking control and this is one way in which you can do that.

There was a time when my daughter seemed to wear a very serious expression upon her face. Her teacher used a series of small simple cartoon faces with broad smiles upon them, placed strategically around the class room to remind all the children that happiness was really only a smile away.

"I smile with the love of life flowing through me. My smile lights up the day for others and when I smile, I become a truly healing light upon the world. Through my happy expression, I lift up my own thoughts and the thoughts of others.

Today is a day of smiles for me".

Choose a day upon which to use your smile, to cultivate the habit of smiling whenever possible, wherever you go, and whatever you may be doing. This is not to say that you will stop when this day is over, simply, that it is the start of something marvellous that can change you and your world. Smiling people tend to be happy people, and happy people are loving and healthy people.

Being smiling and happy does not make you flippant or reckless. You will still be serious about your life, but in a happy, loving way. People often confuse serious application with misery!

Upon your first smiling day, find a picture of a happy smiling face, or a photograph of someone enjoying a really good laugh. If possible, use a photograph of yourself. If no photograph is available, then find or draw a little cartoon face as I described to you earlier, for that will work just as effectively for you.

Attach to your picture, the statement given earlier and read it aloud at the beginning of your day, and at frequent intervals as your day progresses. As you read the statement, look at the picture and just feel the happiness flow through you. Even in the most difficult situation or set of circumstances, such an approach will at least bring a smile to your face, albeit a gentle one.

What is very important to understand here is that this approach, implemented over a period of time, perhaps changing the picture you use occasionally, will begin to change your own magnetism. You will become a centre for more happiness, more smiles. You will attract into your life more events that will fit in with your smile and increased feelings of happiness and well-being. People will like to be in your company and you will like people more and more each day.

I knew a bus conductor who was always smiling and happy, frequently singing as he supervised his passengers. Many an early morning traveller had a smile brought to his face on a cold dark winter morning by this cheerful smiling man. He never seemed to be upset or harassed by difficult people, was polite to everyone, and enjoyed his work and his life. In fact, he truly loved his life, and the people in it.

Eventually, if you adopt the smile approach to life, you will not need a picture or a statement to read, to help you to realign your thinking. You will do it naturally as it becomes imbued in your nature.

Of course, it sometimes appears difficult to smile, when you hurt or are unhappy. But when you learn to smile through apparent adversity, then you will have unlocked one of the great secrets of life. We have become conditioned to frown, to be unhappy, thus feeling that it is the norm, when in fact the converse is true.

Man was meant to be happy and fulfilled. He was intended to bear a smile upon his countenance. Why else would it be relatively effortless and natural to smile and laugh, as opposed to the heavy frown of despondency and woe?

One of my patients discovered the power of smiles and laughter as very potent agents for recovery from depression.

I recommended to him that he select light humorous reading for the very last thing at night and first thing in the morning. We discussed which books and authors he had found amusing in the past and we came up with several titles that he could obtain easily. He then followed my suggestions and almost immediately he reported an increased lightness of mood, and less apprehensive feelings about the forthcoming day. In his own words, he "really enjoyed his little laugh every morning", before getting up to wash and dress. It proved to be a great platform on which to build his recovery and it is a useful idea for all of us to bear in mind.

I have always found humour and laughter very powerful ways to break down barriers and enable happiness and harmony to abound.

Some years ago, I was working with children with

behavioural and learning problems which were often severely handicapping. In fact, the school was in an area of social unrest, and authority in any shape or form was often viewed with suspicion.

During my first term, a light-hearted concert was planned, and it was suggested that I might enjoy producing a "Greek Dance," with some of the boys, with a licence to "work out my own, less ethnic choreography"!

Eventually, I became one of the troupe, frilly skirt and all, and we learned our steps perfectly.

During the first performance of the concert, bemused parents watched as we moved around the large hall to strains of "Zorba's Dance." As the music increased in speed, so too did our steps. Unfortunately, my rather flimsy white skirt tore at the join, leaving me to finish the dance in a rather more exposed, yet decent state, than had been planned.

The reaction of the parents was one of hysterical laughter, which culminated with tremendous applause for the boys, who had indeed worked hard. It was one of those events never to be forgotten and any idea that I lacked a sense of fun or humour, was immediately crushed.

I too, like the parents, saw the funny side of things, and I loved to laugh. Barriers were broken down and friendships grew. In future boys would be honoured to be invited into the "corps de dance" at school concerts!

In situations such as this we find a common denominator to which we can all easily relate. It could be argued that others had no right to laugh at my apparent misfortune — they should have pitied me! But no, the truth is that we should meet and must see the beauty and humour in all things, for only then will we be completely free from tension and able to express our true loving spiritual selves to the world.

I ask you now, to think of a situation where you have made people laugh, smile and be happy. Isolate an occasion where you were responsible for promoting laughter amongst others, whether it was family, friends, neighbours, colleagues or whoever. Think of the joy you brought into their lives at that moment.

Sit quietly, close your eyes, and recapture the occasion as carefully as you can. Remember it clearly, seeing that happy laughter for which you are responsible. You have helped these people so very much.

Your reaction is crucial. If you react with anger, because you feel embarrassed or hurt, then this shows an over sensitivity based upon a lack of love of yourself. If you truly love yourself, you would be happy too. You would see the fun, the lighter side of what has happened.

As I said earlier, this is not to condone the sneering laughter of cruelty. That would be wrong, and those who laugh at pain and real misfortune, are not truly laughing, but rather tensely howling through their warped perception of themselves and all things.

We are talking of the "belly-laugh" that releases tension and promotes a relaxed, loving atmosphere amongst those involved.

When you have considered one such occasion, spend time recalling as many more as you can, re-living the positive, comfortable feeling it brings to you. And when that is done, realise that you love to laugh; that you love happiness and fun; that you can and will see the humour in all things, in a gentle loving fashion.

Resolve to take that feeling with you into life, every day.

"I see humour in all things. Gentle, relaxing fun abounds, and I identify it easily, enjoying the freedom it brings. Humour liberates and so I am loving and free".

I spent some time working in variety and cabaret. I used to love the empty theatre when the audience had left and the lights were down. The laughter lingered on, long, long after the show and, in the quiet, you could feel it all around you.

Recall that we are a mass of vibrations and that we can determine HOW we vibrate. through deep, happy laughter, we can vibrate with a love of life and subsequent health.

I have often heard it said, "A happy man never gets cancer". I must concur with that, and extend the idea to all disease that appears in a life-time.

The truth is that laughter expresses a love of life. And such a powerful lovingness must and will express health, spiritual, emotional, mental and physical health.

Do you know someone who smiles and laughs most of the time? Such people are like gold-dust, usually popular and a pleasure to be with. They will raise the level of feeling in the company of any group or in a household, bringing with them happiness and a relaxed state that all can enjoy.

I have a friend who is very successful in a very competitive area of sales. Whilst other companies find their share of a dwindling market likewise is shrinking, his company finds the opposite is happening, for not only is he positive and instilled with a belief in his products, but he is a happy, genial chap most of the time with a sense of fun and a delightful sense of humour. Company buyers always have time to see him, however busy they are and however bad trade may be.

Many a great lesson has been ignored, many an opportunity lost, because of poor presentation by those teaching.

I learned a lesson from a Catholic priest many years ago, when he visited my hometown as a guest speaker of the local church that my mother attended.

There were many serious points that he was very keen to preach to the local people on various topics, yet his addresses were always prefaced by a light hearted story, and his text was peppered with anecdotes, jokes and other humorous devices to make them interesting and thought provoking. The church was packed with standing room only on every night of his visit.

We all love to laugh.

Someone once told me that his greatest ambition was to start a broadcasting company that offered "alternative News Bulletins". He had quite rightly concluded that all News services tend to be geared to the dissemination of doom and gloom, of misery and tragedy, pain and suffering, war and terror, which of course helps no one, least of all the situation receiving publicity. His idea was to give publicity to happy, and even funny occurrences and events, ignoring the political infighting, strikes and crime. He felt that this would, in time influence people more positively, and help to beat illness such as depression and anxiety neurosis, by gradually making happiness, goodness and laughter the mean by which people will try to live and guage their behaviour and thinking. I think he is right.

The next time you go to the library or consider buying a book, abandon the customary sections of interest a little, and spend time looking through books that are designed to be light-hearted and to make us happy. Not perhaps, some of the more brash and offensive books that can be a little unfunny where considered carefully, but those written with some thought and skill, designed not to hurt or upset anyone. You may be surprised at just how many there are and I am sure you will be pleased with what is available if you continue your search.

There are many cases reported of people being healed by laughter, sometimes of terminal disease and it is now generally acknowledged, that laughter is extremely therapeutic.

Choose to seek out the humorous, the happy in whatever you are doing. When something appears to go wrong, look for the funny view of it, for there will be one that will help to balance things a little.

Most of all, realise that the ability to laugh is the true sign of strength.

People who "fail to see what is so amusing" are usually simply expressing their insecurity about themselves or their beliefs. The ability of the Jewish Nation to laugh at itself has helped it to survive where most others would have crumbled and disintegrated. It is because they took themselves seriously that they were and are able to see the lighthearted side of their customs and attitudes. There is a lesson for us all there.

If ever your pride is hurt; if ever you feel depressed in any way, recall a moment of great humour and laughter in your life. We all experience them, however gloomy we feel our lives are.

Fill your thinking with those funny and uplifting moments, and the gloom will be gradually washed away. And if these moments have occurred in the past, there is absolutely no reason why they will not occur in the future.

I repeat, whatever your situation, what has occurred for your good in the past, can and will occur in the future if you let it do so.

However limited you feel the possibilities are, remember that your view is very restricted and there will certainly be occasions for happiness and laughter in the future, make no mistake about it.

Some of the funniest things happen upon us suddenly "out of the blue", catching us unawares. The Divine Intelligence will always provide us with opportunity.

At a baptism I attended, the child was to be annointed with holy oil. As he performed this part of the ceremony, without losing dignity at all, the priest turned to the father and said, "It's SHELL high viscosity I use; the children seem to like it you know."

Enlightened clergy are often a source of great fun and humour.

One vicar I knew well had a marvellous capacity for seeing the laughter in what perhaps, could be a difficult and nerve jangling occasion.

He told of one visit he made as a visiting minister to another church, where he was to conduct a wedding ceremony. He had arrived a little late so he quickly took off his mackintosh, hanging it in the vestry, and he then commenced to lead the service.

After a few moments he could detect a rather strong scorching smell but he was unsure of its source. The service went on, the congregation sang the first hymn, "Come Down, O Love Divine", and the burning and scorching smell became stronger than ever.

Eventually he realised that he had put his pipe into his coat pocket without extinguishing it first. As he turned toward the vestry he could see the smoke coming from his mackintosh. He acted quickly, summoning a verger to remove his coat and eliminate the problem.

The verger removed the offending pipe and carried the smouldering coat past the incumbent to the churchyard. As he did so, the congregation were singing the first line of the hymn's second verse. It read, "O let it freely burn"!

This man loved to laugh, and could see the humorous side of this own apparent misfortune. He always told his story to young couples wishing to be married by him at his church because it "helped to break the ice."

You must always be prepared to break the ice in your life as you seek out those things that will make you, and others, smile and be happy . . . and healthy.

Start now. Start loving to laugh.

"I seek the happy and humorous in all that I do.
Let me love to laugh, always."

PART 12

YOU ARE BEAUTIFUL (More thoughts)

The next time you see someone you have rather become used to, or see frequently, every day, perhaps call to mind that they are seventy five percent water. That is true! Any scientist will confirm that all human beings are approximately 75% water, with a few other bits and pieces thrown in for good measure.

Now, don't stare for too long, in fact, don't stare at all but just think of the above statement and its basic implications and then its real absurdity, as you see the changes in expression on their face, and the variety of possibilities of movement in even the most aged and infirm body. Try this briefly with everyone; husband or wife, children, parents, close friends and so on.

What will emerge is a new sense of wonder. You will begin to see that, however imperfect your vision of life has been before; however pointless or finite things may have appeared to you, those animate beings around you, called people, are truly incredible pieces of technology. Whatever blemishes or weaknesses they have in their physical bodies, they are really quite amazing and truly beautiful. In some mysterious way they are able to harmonise and structure all those volatile chemicals and elements to produce this mobile, thinking, feeling and discerning creature. What is it within this animate being that makes it work, have form and prevent it from drooping and collapsing into a mass of purposeless protoplasm?

It is the Divine Idea called man, which expresses the being of the creator in individual form. What you are perceiving is a facet of God, moving about you and seeking to give physical substance or reality to Him. Yet, of course, it is more than this.

All the life you see around you is also a part of you. For All of God, all the attributes of the Infinite Intelligence, dwell within all of you, all of the time. You are not just a part of the Divine, but rather, you are the Divine.

Each atom in the physical structure of those people you see, has the total and completeness of God within it. All of God is within all of you, all of the time.

Now, of course, it is a fact that the physical expression of God is limited by the finite nature of your physical body. Your physical body is a transient entity, and so there is a restriction as to how much of God can show at any one time.

But as we, truly grow nearer and nearer to the creative flow of God, which is creative love, so that expression of his nature becomes more and more enriched, more and more refined and more and more clear in each cell and atom of our being. In a sense we are God's in the making assuming, day by day, moment by moment, our true potential, and our heritage.

Now glance at your own reflection, just briefly. Scientifically speaking, you too, are 75% water. But, deep within, you know that is not true. You know that you are a vast and mysterious Kingdom, largely uncharted by man's forays in his search to understand and conquer.

You are all of God.

Think about that for a moment. You are all of God. God is omnipotent, omniscient, and omnipresent.

Have another glance at that reflection of yourself, then read this statement to yourself three times:

"All of God is within me. My potential is without limit. I am truly a beautiful vehicle for the Flow of love, for God is love and that is who I am". "Be still and know that I am God" Ps. 46 v. 10.

Take that statement with you into the stillness and use it as a platform for your concentration and meditation for a week.

When love shows in every cell in your body, you will be healthy. There is absolutely no other possibility. That is not to say that you must feel guilt if you hurt somewhere at the moment. It is just that you have blocked the flow of love at that point, temporarily, and you can soon do something to rectify that.

We are meant to live happy, healthy lives. I believe that the learning we do through pain is truly a sad way to achieve growth and essentially showing a lack of rhythm in our lives.

We talk, so often, of suffering being good for the soul. In other words, the "allowing" of pain and disease is good for us. The shedding of tears, and anguished cries of the afflicted are desirable?

I can see, and I'm sure you can too, that man can be a very, very slow learner. I can recall many heavy cigarette smokers, who complain of the nuisance of excess catarrh, shortness of breath, and hacking cough, yet make little or no attempt to stop poisoning their beautiful temples, those remarkable bodies, that do seek to be well and whole.

Within our industries, we spend much time seeking methods for the "safe" disposal of poisonous chemicals and toxic waste, which are the by-products of supposedly necessary processes. But are they really necessary?

I used to teach in a school near to a chemical factory which produced synthetic flavours and fragrances for the food and cosmetic industries. On some days, when there was little breeze, the foul odours hung in the air, saturating every breath taken by the local community, and finding its way into every corner of my classroom. This was an intolerable price to pay for the production of totally unnecessary chemicals, designed to titilate man's palate, and assuage his vanity.

Remember that you are truly beautiful. Never lose sight of the fact that you are remarkable, and have a capacity to love and be loved, the like of which will transform you, your life and your world, bringing untold peace and serenity in its wake.

You are going to give love and receive it, every day. You are now magnetised to that end. It is your real discipleship.

I can see, through my own children, a new generation being born who will not tolerate uncaring, harmful habits and standards in their world. They are allergic to chemical additives and pollutants, in their foods, household products, and their whole environment. They will not be happy and at peace until their world is purified and balanced. They are the children of the New Age, ready to meet life face to face, seeking not to hide anything, but to be open and honest, caring and loving.

There is optimism and hope in my heart. Let it dwell in your heart too.

Use the ideas in this work which is dedicated to love. Fall in love with love. Unashamedly talk of it, give it and live it, and express your own beauty to others. Let your light shine Learn the statements from the book. Keep them about you, write them down everywhere you can.

Start to create your own statements on love, and make a scrapbook of quotes from others on the idea of true, unselfish love. Wade through the dross of the press and seek out loving statements and ideas for they are there, obscured though they may be.

Send loving thoughts to everyone in your world, and claim your place as a Child of light, seeking to bring good into the lives of others.

Claim perfect health and always remember that "Being Loving is Being Healthy".

"And I saw a new heaven and a new earth; for the first heaven and the first earth were passed away."

Rev 21. 1

PART 13

AFFIRMATIONS AND STATEMENTS

The sometimes repetitive nature of this book and the statements with it, is quite deliberate. It is through repetition that our consciousness can be raised and positive, loving, and constructive ideas etched upon our minds so that old, negative habits are diluted and washed away, redundant, as things of the past.

These statements are now listed for your convenience. Add to them and adapt them if you wish, so that they help you as much as they possibly can. A good thing can never be said frequently enough.

"From head to toe
My body is filled with love.
From my head to my toes
I have my body working for me.
Love circulates throughout me from my heart,
Ever flowing
Warming and caressing every tissue,
Every fibre and every cell in my body.
All the organs of my body are working
So well for me.
I am filled with health giving love.
My body is fed and cleansed beautifully,
as the creative breath of life fills me,
renewing and restoring.
I thank and bless my body with love
From my head to my toes."

"There is one creative power in the Universe. It is a loving creative, good power that builds the perfect ideas of form and shape, and colour. It creates the flowers and trees, the birds and animals. It is only man's negative attitudes and actions that bring deformity. I am part of this perfect, creative, loving power. I can achieve all that I need to achieve in my life."

"I express only love. I speak love of myself and my affairs. I give good creative worth to all that I tackle. In shortchanging a task or action, I shortchange myself. I see only love, and I express only love. I speak only love, for I love life, and I am life."

"I start my day with love. Today is a day of opportunity for me. All good things will come my way. I deserve them and say thank you."

"I bless the day I have been given. I am thankful for the things I have accomplished, in a good, loving and perfect way."

"I recognise and give thanks for these things done for me this day. I see in them the true flow of creative love, expressing as service to me. I know that more and more good things will happen for me tomorrow, and each new day in perfect loving ways."

"I am more and more attuned to the loving power of creation in my world. I give thanks for it and bless it, as it sends its healing and harmonising love to me."

"I bless my world. I send out my love to my environment in waves of never ending power. I give thanks for the love and care I receive from all that I can see. Every part of my world surrounds me with loving care. No harm will ever come to me from the things I live amongst. They offer me their never ending love in the power and glory of creation. I accept it and give my love to all things. I love and bless my world. I act and think in loving ways. I am considerate and thoughtful in my deeds and actions. I see my world as a part of me, I love and bless my world and all around me."

"Every task that I undertake, I do so to help my fellow man. Everything I do is to help life go along in a smooth and happy way. Everything I do is important and I choose to do it with love, to the best of my ability.

Whenever I do something in haste, or in a hurry, just to get through it, I devalue the present moment and so I devalue myself.

I now see that all things, however small, are important for me and for others, so I do all things with love and care."

"I love and bless that which is given to me to eat and drink. It is imbued with the loving power that created me and all living things, and I give thanks for that which is given to me. I thank those who have enabled these good things to come to me, and I send them thoughts of love. I love and bless these fruits of goodness, and the life with which they bless me."

"I eat only that which I need. I eat only that which is good for me. I love to be my healthy ideal weight, at all times. I eat only that which I need. A loving me, is a healthy me. A healthy me is a perfect me, at my ideal body weight."

"I love my healthy body, and the healthy diet I have."

"I recognise each event in my life as an opportunity. I understand that Universal love flows through me, touching all things and all people I meet along my path. People, animals, events and circumstances, I touch them all with love, and I make my way a happy and enriching one.

There is nothing I meet in my day that I cannot manage. All things become possible as I flow with love, and I meet my good in all situations and people, feeling safe, secure and confident."

"My journey is God's journey. I drive secure in the love of Infinite Wisdom. I do no harm to others, and others do no harm to me, as we are all protected, journeying upon God's loving road."

"I am safe and happy, as I journey with my friend. He is guided by the flow of creative Wisdom and Love, and takes me perfectly to my destination."

"The food I prepare, I bless with love, to enrich those who partake of it. I offer all food as a gift, to bless the lives of others as we share the wonderful bounty of creation."

"I make this call with a powerful loving heart, expecting and knowing I shall experience the perfect response."

"This task is worthy of my best attention and I treat it so."

"I am a child of creation. I have power to be all that I seek to be. I link with the loving flow of life and turn that love to flow through me. And as the love pours through my heart, I know I love myself deeply and sincerely. Like the blades of grass in the meadow, I too am a part of a Great Living tapestry, important and needed. I see myself as a true spark of Love, vibrant and free, glowing and peaceful.
I choose love and love the "I" that is me."

"I give all the qualities of my soul opportunity to grow. I speak with wisdom, I listen with care. I enjoy good, right action in my life and reflective, calm moments of consideration. I express balance in all things."

"My sense of Oneness with the creative Power that makes all things, grows, moves and radiates as a light all around me. This inner love touches the hearts and minds of others, and I am protected and loved, secure within its Power. I am cradled in its beauty.
I choose to abandon ways of judgement and criticism.
I throwoff hates and resentments.
I become a loving soul, as is my right place within the Divine Design, and I forgive and heal both myself and those I meet, expressing the love I feel within me now."

"I accept the forgiving love that pours out to me. I welcome it and embrace it. I know that I am forgiven, as I forgive. I am free, and express the loving health that freedom brings, and say thank you for it, as it manifests in my life, each and every day."

"New life starts within me now. Like the lilies of the Field, I grow, and I am given all that I need. I forgive, I love and I grow."

"There is a part of me in everyone else and a part of them in me."

"I have no enemies. The healing power of love flows through me to those who need it most. They are warmed and caressed in its light and its gentle strength. Hate and fear are dissolved, and melt away like snow in warm sunlight. The Love I express will return to me enriched, more powerful than before. I am free and they are free now. And it is so."

"I dedicate my life to service. In all that I do from today, I seek to serve. It is my desire to uplift, inspire and bring peace. I offer myself for acts of true service, and I am alert to every opportunity that comes my way."

"All life is one. I see all created things as important, and I appraoch them with an open and loving heart. An open, loving heart is a powerful heart. It is invincible. Others return that which they receive and experience. I set the wheels in motion. I heal my life, now, and I heal the lives of others."

"As I seek improvement for myself, I recognise its perfect manifestation at the right time, in the right place, in the right way. It is so."

"I attune to all ideas of purity and goodness, and I am wrapped and sustained in Divine Light."

"I am the light of the world.
I am the light of the world.
My flame burns bright with love and with peace.
And I am now Love in the world".

"My Real-Self is my Creator expressing through me. I am
Him and He is me. There is no separation only unity, as it
flows as love in my life.
Perfect love feeds me daily in endless supply, and as I share
love and give love, it grows, allowing heaven to establish
here on earth.
And I heal the earth; and I heal all things and so, too, am I
healed."

"I am unique. I have a role to play, that is perfect and right
for me, and I am given all that I need to accomplish it."

"Teach me the ways of Truth, to love, to serve and to heal.
Bring me closer with each moment to the flowering of Peace
within me. That I will be a light for mankind, to see clearly
the ways of perfect Harmony in all the affairs of the world."

"I now show the Divine Pattern in my life. Perfect
expression of my true potential now flowers and comes into
my affairs. And it is so."

"All of God is within me. My potential is without limit. I
am a truly beautiful vehicle for the flow of love, for God is
love, and that is who I am."

"Be still and know that I am God."

"I see you perform that perfect function for which you are
designed, and for that I thank you. All ideas of disease are
gone and the light of love illuminates every dark corner.
You and I are one, and so express that perfect wholeness of
being. And it is so."

"Within me is wonder and majesty.
Within me is power and love.
Within me are all the secrets and answers for all
that I need to know."

"When I smile, I become a healing light, uplifting the
thoughts of others."

"I seek the happy and humorous in all that I do. Let me
love to laugh, always."

"Perfect love smiles."

"I listen to the voice within and perfect answers come."

Paul Lambillion's 'HEALING IMAGES'

SELF-HELP and WELL-BEING in sounds, words and music on cassettes.

"BREATHE, RELAX AND IMAGINE" £5.50
A simple and effective approach to breath awareness, relaxation and peace of mind, including marvellous guided imagery and music. (C10841)

"PICTURE YOURSELF RELAXED" £5.00
Two twenty minute sequences, one for morning and one for evening, designed to bring a more positive yet tranquil state of being. (C08841)

"YOU ARE THE POWER" £5.50
An antidote to fear, worry and depression, through advice, practical techniques and meditation. (C05852)

"A PATHWAY TO HEALING" £5.95
Looks at reasons why we become ill, and steps we can take to help ourselves. Included is a beautiful, positive, self-healing meditation. (C02851)

"SLEEP PEACEFULLY" £5.00
Sound advice and approaches to encourage a good night's rest and to help overcome insomnia. Features a relaxing, guided descent into sleep, and a brief follow-up for the morning. (C07851)

"GARDEN OF PEACE" £5.00
A gentle, peaceful stroll through the Garden of the Mind, meditating upon Life, Love, Joy and Peace. (C05851)

"JEWELS & GEMSTONES" £5.00
Two lovely, magical journeys in the imagination, created especially for children aged from 6 years upwards, which promote a confident, relaxed and happy frame of mind enhancing creative thought and a sense of well-being.
(C02852)

"*THEMES I*"   £5.00
A mixture of light, varied, musical ideas and themes from
Geoff McCann, played on guitar and synthesizer.
                                                        (C010842)

"*INTRODUCING HEALING IMAGES*"   £1.95
A brief introductory cassette, with extracts from five titles.
                                                        (C07852)

"*YOU CAN DO IT/STOP WORRYING*"   £5.00
Two guided meditations designed to improve self-image,
curb worrying, and motivate to confident, peak performance
in any task or activity.   (C10851)

"*CONTROL YOUR WEIGHT*"   £5.50
This commonsense advice given, and the relaxation imagery
provide a powerful tool in the quest for correct eating and
ideal bodyweight.   (C02861)

The '*HEALING IMAGES*' Cassettes are written and
presented by PAUL LAMBILLION,
with music by Geoff McCann.

Available from L. N. Fowler & Co. Ltd.